In the Beginning

Creation Myths from Around the World

The fourteen stories in this book are available in mp3 audio format, read by actress Amy Walker. Listen to the *Creation Myths from Around the World* while you are driving, commuting, resting... Go to www.findhornpress.com to purchase and download.

In the Beginning

Creation Myths from Around the World

Stories *re-told by*

CAROLYN NORTH

Artwork by

ADRIENNE ROBINSON

ICRL Press

Princeton, New Jersey

Dedicated to our children and grandchildren

Photographs by Adrienne Robinson and Susan Wilson
Graphic Design: Sara Glaser, with Carolyn
Graphic Production: Laura Smyth

For other books by Carolyn North, or to contact the
authors, go to: www.healingimprovisations.net

ICRL Press
468 N. Harrison St.
Princeton, NJ 08540-3511

ISBN 13: 978-1-936033-02-7
ISBN 10: 1-936033-02-X

Contents

Introduction

"…then a throb, a pulse, an urge, a flutter of love—an impulse or desire in the ocean of consciousness to create and enjoy, a pulse that emanates from everywhere at once. From that initial movement, the whole world comes into being. This ocean of consciousness is the Absolute; the throb is its creative power…"

From a creation hymn of the
Kashmiri Hindu Shaivites

IN THE BEGINNING *Creation Myths from Around the World* was also born in a throb of desire to create and enjoy—just like the world. Adrienne Robinson and I, friends for over thirty years, have collaborated to re-tell and illustrate creation myths of many cultures according to the oldest, most indigenous sources we could find. Oftentimes, it was the fragments and vivid hints off to the side of the more popular versions that lit the way back to a deeper past, and when they rang true, we brought them into the stories.

For three years we read masses of source material, researched cultures and their art forms, and told each other the myths until we could feel our way to the indigenous mind and aesthetic. Adrienne researched the traditional art from each culture, working to interpret respectfully each culture's style and history in her piece, while I tried to stay true to the meaning and feel for the stories of each culture, in my own language.

Since we live on opposite sides of the country, we would meet periodically in some beautiful place and spend an intensive week together working. On the banks of streams and in leafy woods I would read the new story aloud while Adrienne sat back, eyes closed, watching images flash across her mind's eye. Then the new art piece would reveal itself and, in the course of the week, emerge into the forms pictured here, from masks and felt-fabric capes to rice-paper hangings, wire sculptures and goatskin puppets. Ordinary objects were used—paper, wire, fabrics, nuts, seeds, animal skins—to capture the sense of who these people were, and how they understood the creation of the world and their own beginnings.

According to our sources, Creation was not a one-time event, but continues to emerge from the Universal field of potential—called by many names in many cultures—all the time. The Creation never stops speaking, and its language has no bounds. It speaks through all of existence, all the time; it speaks through us.

In these times of disruption and change, it seems that if we are to survive—both as a planet and as a species—we humans will have to be as flexible, innovative and creative as we can be. What may appear to be fearsome roadblocks in our individual and collective lives might have to be thought of as opportunities to do things differently. Instead of slogging yet again through old, unworkable situations, we might surprise ourselves by dreaming up new solutions to those old problems, re-thinking them from a larger, more experimental perspective. We can use our dilemmas as opportunities to create anew—every day in every way—the world in which we wish to live.

Adrienne and I discovered just how much fun that was! When we were dreaming up the artworks for these myths, we decided to use ordinary, commonly available materials in extraordinary ways, so that the medium would itself be the message. We wanted to show that the creative process was available to people of every age and place. We wished the artworks to demonstrate that everything in the world is potential material out of which art—or life—can be created.

The giant spiral for *First Mother*, for example, was made entirely from natural objects picked up during walks, from grains in our kitchens, from the trees in our backyards: seeds, pods, nuts, shells, leaves, bone. Adrienne even included the remains of a wasps' nest that we had, to our stinging misfortune, disturbed during one of our forays! What had been a pile of throwaways became a stunning work of art. As did the wire sculptures depicting the Egyptian god Ptah, and the pre-Celtic *Miria*, both of which began as an ordinary spool of utility wire from the hardware store. We had the best time! As Adrienne put it, "I'm having so much fun, I'm afraid I might get arrested!"

The creation myths here depict the world
as beginning in a fathomless, timeless,
Void—an ineffable darkness, a nothingness
which contains the consciousness to yearn
for more. This yearning is what shakes the
motionless Void into motion, and that initial
movement is what sets the whole thing out
of its equilibrium into a shimmying dance
of new possibilities. Beings are born from
the darkness, and they beget Earth and Sky,
mountains and forests. Into their creation
emerge plants and animals who slither, crawl,
walk, run, swim, fly; who live, laugh, fight,
love and die, and beget the next generations
of their species to people the Earth.

All these stories seem to be telling us that
every one of us is a Creator, all the time, and
anything we can imagine can be brought into
existence by our having
the courage and will to do so.

It is time. By collaborating with each other
and collaborating with the Earth, all of us
can help create the next phase of this many-
layered, multi-dimensioned and miraculous
world we call ours.

Carolyn North and Adrienne Robinson

The Song of Creation
Genesis

*I*n the Beginning, there simply *was*. What There Was had no shape, no size, no color, no form. There was neither Time nor Space, neither Birth nor Death.

It was like a Thought without a Thinker. It was like a Knowing without a Knower.

It was not Male and it was not Female; it was neither Young nor Old. But it was more than either Male or Female, and its age was Eternity.

This intelligent Energy, this paradox rich with potential but so difficult to name has been called by many *The Creator*.

Longing for a World born from Itself, *The Creator* breathed in, and sighed. *Ahhhhmm…*

That sound, like a song sung into the silence, shook the perfect stillness into motion. And from the primordial Balance, movement was begun.

The Creator sang, and What There Was, for the first time, danced.

"Let Sound," sang the voice, "be as Light!"

And from the Song and the Dance there was Light.

Just as beauty is created from the vision and imagination of the artist's being, so was the World brought forth from the Intelligence of *The Creator's* being.

Improvising, *The Creator* spun the Elements from the seamless Source of Itself.

The Dance whirled out from the Dancer; the Song emerged from the Singer.

The birthing Cosmos expanded and contracted. It twirled like a whirlwind of Light and Sound and burst, rushing into Air.

The winds of Air, fanning the Light into Heat Unimaginable, flamed into Fire.

Hissing, the Fire ignited Air into steamy vapor which condensed into Water.

And the Water, dried by the winds and Fire, hardened into Earth.

Dark and dense with Matter, its dance stately and its song low, the Earth settled weightily upon the waters.

And the Light lifted to claim the sky, luminous upon the dark Earth.

Light and Dark, Matter and Spirit pulsed to *The Creator's* subtle breath, dancing together in perfect rhythm the Cosmic Dance.

Light…Dark…Day…Night…Spirit… Matter…

And Time entered to dance its measured steps upon the stage of Space.

Light…Dark…Day…Night…Spirit… Matter…

All was in motion and All was in balance. *The Creator* breathed out with the completion of the First Movement, and was well pleased.

For it was good.

Sun and Moon filled the Firmament, and stars, galaxies and roving planets. Clouds gathered, and winds blew across the ruffled waters, carrying rain.

Light…Dark…Day…Night….Day…Night…

And there was Lightning and Thunder! The rains poured down upon the Earth!

Rivers raged in torrents down the barren mountains, dissolving hardness, bringing the dust of the land to the sea.

Fiery cauldrons erupted boiling magma from the deeps of the Earth, spewing fertile ash into the quenching Air.

Day…Night…Day…Night…Day…Night…

The Dance was wild with energy, and the Song roared into the Air!

Sparked by The Creation Itself, Matter was thrown into the dance of Change.

Every thrust inspired a new improvisation; every tumble led to another Idea.

The Earth quaked, subsided—and lakes formed in the hollows.

Snow fell on high peaks—and glaciers were born.

Rushing rivers dug deep gorges—and new land spread out at the sea.

The World was ecstatic in its Dance, and *The Creator* was in love with Itself creating.

That Love echoed outwards from The Center, like a sun's heat shimmering across a changing landscape.

The Creator's love lit the waters and the winds, the mountains and the molten depths.

It spread to the far-flung galaxies and it rested, tenderly, upon the tiny pebbles of the shore.

And receiving the blessing of *The Creator*, the World in turn loved Itself.

Day…Night…Day…Night…Day…Night…

Hidden in the shallows of sun-warmed seas, amidst the brothy reefs close to the shore, a shaft of light penetrated just so, catching a tumbled bit of debris that was ready for the spark.

Like a torch to kindling, Life took hold and spread, fed by itself, enclosed by itself.

The whole World held its breath and, in that moment, was changed forever.

Life had been created by The Creation Itself—out of Love.

The Second Movement was achieved.

The stage was set; the lifeline in place. The World was a wonder and All Creation was well pleased.

For it was good.

Longing for softness *The Creator*, with a leap of imagination, dreamed up Green.

From the sun-heated shallows, the slime of Life crept up towards the beach, spreading from reef-rock to dry land. Molecule by molecule, it sucked moisture from stone and breathed energy from the sun, crumbling hard rock into soil and covering the land with a fuzz of lichen-green.

Day…Night…Day…Night…Day…Night…

Grasses sprouted and grew in that soil, threading root-webs that softened the land still more. The ferns appeared, and the trees; the shrubs and twisting vines.

Each plant found its niche. Each plant took its chance to put down roots into the Earth and reach up towards the Sun.

Stems and tendrils and branches leafed out in greens of every shade. The land throbbed with growth, its great green breaths perfuming the wind and transforming the very Air itself.

Each plant opened the way for others: fungi appeared and succulents; water-lilies and tree ferns, all branching out from each other, all changing the land.

Nights followed days and seasons cycled through seasons.

Plants budded, burst into green leaf and then, when their season was passed, dried back into brown. Dropping their seeds and spores, they over wintered in deep ground until the next burgeoning spring.

Death came into being, and rebirth.

Generations of plants cycled through seasons of ripening and decay, each at its own pace, each in its own scale of Time.

Connected by a living web, all were entwined with the rhythm of the others. And each was in time with the Sun.

The Third movement was accomplished.

Life had taken root. *The Creator* was both the Dreamer and the Dreamed and loved the creation, which was Itself.

For it was good.

Sunlight met rain and across the sky a rainbow was flung, its colors arching high above the greens of the jungle.

Responding, *The Creator* imagined reds and oranges, yellows and purples and blues, and playfully began to experiment with flowers!

And how the plants bloomed!

They unfurled petals and pistils, blossoming riotously in every hue. Violet orchids appeared, pink-edged jasmine, sunflower and rose. Golden buttercups dotted meadows and orange lilies lined the green banks of streams.

The World was ablaze with fragrant color shimmering to be noticed.

And in the cold ground hints of insects, still unformed, warmed to the lure of the flowers and began blooming as well. They sprouted legs and segments, pincers and wings— anything that could help them buzz their way towards the enticing flowers.

There they nuzzled greedily, plunging their brittle bodies into the spicy bright cups and sucking ecstatically such sweet nectar…

And from blossom to blossom they flitted, feeding,
sowing with their bodies the flowers' precious, sticky seed.

The game was on! In their elegant tango together, the insects and the flowers played out The Creation's love for Itself, and made it their own!

For in their intimate dance, each survived only with the help of the other.

O cunning insects!

O seductive flowers!

Long before the World made a special thing of Sex, you were already courting each other with ardor, passionately yearning for union.

Days followed nights and nights followed days until a new song came drifting on the currents of a breeze:

If Air makes for flight and Dark makes for Night,

Then what shall we see in the springs of the Sea?

"It's swimmers we will see!" swooshed the winds upon the waves.

And the fishes appeared, at one with the water, swimming.

Scaled and streamlined, they flicked their fins through waters shallow and deep.

Breathing through slit gills, they were flat, they were round; transparent as jellyfish or tough-shelled as limpets. Swarming in quick schools, they ate or got eaten each according to its own kind.

Their blood was cold, and salt as the sea. Their pulse matched the rhythms of tides, moon and surf.

What had been empty ocean was now soupy with Life, from the tidelines to the depths.

And Life spilled into the rivers, the lakes and the streams.

The Fourth Movement was done. Life now inhabited the waters.

And *The Creator* was well pleased, for it was good.

Air and Sea were now filled, but the land, with all its lush vegetation, was still empty of creatures.

A few scaly ones, stranded by the tides, lay gasping on the sands, exposed. Some learned to breathe air, and survived.

Slowly, they dragged themselves inland to bask on hot, noonday rocks, warming their blood with the Sun.

Day…Night…Day…Night…Day…Night…

In a gulp of Inspiration, some reptiles learned to swallow the Sun!

Their blood coursed warm through their limbs, freeing them to move farther afield.

They grew feathers, they grew fur; tails and haunches and snouts. On four legs they crawled and scampered, trotted and leapt, feeding on grasses and leaves and each other.

The birds spread out wings and took to the air, singing.

Sparrows fluttered and pink flamingos clustered in quiet lagoons. Raptors and ravens, bluejays and seagulls swooped low and flew high, riding wind currents, riding.

Males and females of every species mated, multiplied. Their offspring filled forests and jungles, mountain slopes and prairies. The steppes echoed with their hoofbeats; savannas resounded with their calls, and the high, thin cries of their young.

Some warm-blooded ones went back to the Sea, and the waters churned with spinning dolphins and migrating whales.

Everywhere the Earth responded to their animal presence, and the land was forever changed. The mammals had inherited the Earth.

The Fifth Movement of The Creation was achieved.

The chorus was sung by voices in every range, loud and clear.

And it was good.

A mist went up from the Earth.

And in that mist came a still, small voice singing for the completion of Itself.

The Creator desired that the World be peopled by beings as conscious of themselves as It was conscious
of Itself.

It wished for an image of Eternity fleshed in human form.

From the soils of every land was humankind sculpted: dark soil and light; dense mud and fine silt; yellow and red dust.

Reflecting the Cosmos and sparked with its Spirit, the new beings of the Earth learned speech and cultivation, reason and will, self-governance and ritual. And the care for each other.

They peopled the continents—all genders, all races, all languages, all temperaments.

Cycling from generation to generation, they lived and they loved and they died, emerging from the Wholeness at birth, and returning to the Wholeness at death.

And power was given—power given in trust—for the sacred task of stewarding the Earth and all that lived upon it.

With honor was the trust accepted, and gratitude.

For the privilege of walking upon the sentient and beautiful Earth, the humans pledged to take care of their World and maintain it in Balance. They vowed to uphold its interconnections and support its natural order.

They promised to love the World as they loved themselves.

It was done. Not one thing was lacking; not one thing superfluous.

And the Whole World, abundant with every living form imaginable to The Creation sang out in chorus its wonder and thanks.

In thunders and splashes, gurgles and whirs and barks; with words and laughter and screeches, squeals and bleats; with hisses and whinnies and snorts and howls and crashes and murmurs—the Universe sang!

Grace abounded, and All Creation was very well pleased.

Bowing to The Creation as Itself, the Song that had sung the World into being completed its Sixth Movement.

And breathed.

And when the Song was a long, sustained hum with all voices blending in perfect harmony, The Creator held the Seventh Movement as a rest.

And it was **very** *good.*

Sky Woman
Iroquois Nation

In the Beginning, there was only Sky above and Water below. Earth had not yet been created.

The Sky realm contained all that would one day exist upon earth, but everything was made of light and the people were like shining elder brothers.

Sky Woman was there, and Sky Chief. And in the center of their world was the Cosmic Tree with glowing berries and fruits.

Sky Woman felt the sound of voices murmuring under her heart and knew she was nearing her time to deliver a child.

She dreamed she saw the tall Tree falling, and she told her husband her dream. Sky Chief knew that dreams express the soul's meanings, and he went with her to the Tree to reassure her that it was strongly rooted with its roots splayed in the four directions.

"See?" he exclaimed, tugging with all his might at the Tree. "See—it cannot be uprooted!"

But as he pulled at the Tree's trunk, it gave way and toppled over, knocking him backwards and creating a great hole where the roots had been.

Sky Woman could see through the darkness to the water in the world below. She leaned over, closer and closer to the edge of the hole, fascinated by this strange darkness, feeling the currents of new winds and smelling the faraway sea.

"Oh!" she cried as she lost her footing. Scrambling to keep from falling, she made a desperate grab for the Tree. But she came away only with a handful of fruits and berries as she slipped out of the lit Sky Realm and plunged downwards through darkness towards the world below.

Wind whipped her hair in every direction and knocked the breath out of her as she fell. Far below, several Loons were winging their way over the water and as they gazed up they saw a ball of light coming swiftly towards them from the Sky.

"*Oooh…oooh,*" they cried, linking their outspread wings to catch what they thought was a falling star. But as it got closer, they recognized the falling light as a sacred woman descending from the Sky.

"*Oooh…oooh,*" they called again, summoning help from Toad, Beaver, Turtle and Muskrat.

Sky Woman heard their mournful cry echo across the waters, and saw the water creatures swimming to where the Loons were making ready to receive her.

Her descent was cushioned by the feathery cloud of the Loons, and when she landed softly and opened her eyes, Toad and Beaver and Muskrat and Turtle were all surrounding her, blinking in amazement.

"What do we do now?" asked the Loons. "She cannot fly and she cannot swim. And she's heavy!"

"She needs a place to stand and I can support her," said Turtle. "Place her on my back. And you, Beaver, dive deep into the water and scoop up some mud to make an earth."

Beaver dove with a splash and was gone. They waited. Sky Woman protectively held her pregnant belly and looked around at her new world.

And they waited.

"The water is very deep," explained Turtle, worried that Beaver might not have been able to reach bottom. At last Beaver surfaced, unsuccessful.

"It was too far down for me…" he gasped.

Muskrat went next, paddling first in a circle and then diving swiftly. Again they waited. And waited.

But Muskrat also returned with empty paws.

So Toad went down, plopping in and kicking hard. She was gone longer than the others— so long they feared she may have drowned in the attempt to bring up mud to make the earth, but just as they had given up hope, a bedraggled and near-dead Toad came up spluttering.

And crammed in her jaw was a ball of mud from the bottom of the ocean.

"Ah!" said Turtle, removing the mudball from Toad's mouth. "This is enough to start an earth."

Sky Woman spread the mud by walking around and around the edges of Turtle's shell, throwing her power ahead of her. The more

Inside view of mask—first opening.

mud she spread, the more mud there was, and soon Turtle's back was covered, and growing.

He grew to the size of a small island, and then to the size of a big island. When Turtle was as large as North America, Sky Woman stopped walking.

Unaccustomed to so much weight, Turtle stretched and the island shook. Sky Woman dropped her handful of fruits and berries onto Turtle Island and the earth sighed.

After that was done, she said, "It is my time now. Under my heart I hear the murmurs of two voices. My two boys will prepare the earth for all the beings that will follow."

And she lay down on Turtle's back to give birth.

The first son, Sapling, was born, and she suckled him at her right breast. Then her womb rippled with the insistence of his twin, Flint, who was in such a hurry to be born that he tore his way out through his mother's other side.

She gave a sharp cry, turned over in pain and with Flint's birth, she died.

Flint was a rascal from the beginning. Everything Sapling did, Flint tried to undo.

When Sapling placed Sky Woman's head in the Sky to make the Sun, Flint immediately created dry and sandy deserts. When Sapling fashioned the Moon and stars, Flint created darkness.

When Sapling buried the rest of their mother's sacred body and grew corn and beans and pumpkins there for the first people, Flint was quick to create thorns and brambles and gnarled, stunted trees.

When Sapling made green woodlands filled with deer and bear and buffalo, Flint countered with swamps and rocky cliffs, mosquitoes and poisonous snakes

When Sapling made clear rivers filled with fish, Flint created an upstream to make it harder to paddle, and placed sharp, tiny bones in the fish.

Like this, they goaded each other on well into manhood, until the world had everything it needed to be ready for humans—and also much that it didn't need.

"Before we make men and women," said Sapling, "we'd better have one final contest. Whoever is able to move a mountain is the Chief of the people.

Whoever cannot, has to agree to go down into a dark cave and always obey the Chief."

Flint agreed, certain he would win.

He went first, trying with all his might to move the mountain. But it would not budge.

Sapling won't be able to move it either, he thought.

But behind him he heard the huge crunching of rocks as the mountain creaked and rumbled towards Sapling.

He was so surprised that he spun around suddenly, smashing his face against the side of the mountain and dislocating his nose.

"Ow!" he cried, cradling his aching face in his hands.

It was clear he was the loser, and would not be the Chief of the earth.

But Sapling, a gentle and good man, seeing his wounded brother in pain, said,

"Instead of going down into a dark cave, now that you know what it feels like to hurt, stay here and help heal the people. Will you do that?"

"I will—if I have to," replied Flint, a glint of mischief in his eyes. "I can interpret dreams, as well. Bet you didn't know that. And I can control the winds…"

Sapling sighed at his incorrigible brother, and together they scooped up some fragrant red clay from the earth, felt it sticky and pliable in their hands, and began shaping the first human beings.

Inside view of mask—second opening.

A Dream Dreaming Us
African Bushman

At first, before anything existed on top of the earth, there was, underneath, a tiny invisible egg hidden in the soil, dreaming of what would one day be. And the whole spirit of the universe lay coiled inside it.

All the things of Creation were there—plants and animals, men and women, sun and moon and stars, wind and rain, hills and plains and all the great and small waters.

The dream taking place under the ground had no tomorrows and no yesterdays. It was never hot or cold nor were the people ever hungry or sick.

And they did not die.

After the long sleep, the spirit of creation felt a *tap-tapping* in the egg. Feeling hungry to make a world, it pushed against the walls of the shell. The tiny eggshell began to bulge and crack, bulge and crack. And then—POP!—a slimy, little worm hatched and wriggled its way through the earth and up into the air.

It looked around with bright, attentive eyes.

Strong green wings sprang from its body.

It lifted off the ground and grew four long, jointed legs. *Click! Click!*

And two more feet sprouted out in front, lifting as if in prayer.

It was Praying Mantis—the Great Spirit of the World inside a brittle insect body.

Inside his little green body he felt a *tap-tapping*, and he dreamed intently of great waters and small.

Click! Click!

The ocean sprang into being, and springs and lakes.

Click! Click!

Mountains rose from the desert, and rocky hills.

Click! Click!

Gold-green grass, and reeds and shrubs and trees came into being. Mantis felt the *tap-tapping-* inside himself and made fruits to grow on trees and tubers to grow in the earth. Nuts and berries sprang onto branches, and melons swelled from vines.

Click! Click!

Mantis dreamed a great tree, and it sprang from the earth, spreading its roots deep and lifting its branches high. The roots went down to where Mantis' dream of people and animals, sun, moon and stars still lived.

Sitting very still in prayer position, he cocked his head and listened for the people and the animals.

When he felt them *tap-tapping* inside him, he dug a hole into the ground near the great tree to reach them.

He dug until he could see their underground world, and then he called,

"First -woman -of- all- women! Come!"

The first- woman-of-all- women heard herself named and, hand over hand, she climbed up through the dark soil until she reached the air of the world.

She felt the warmth of the sun on her body. She smelled the sweetness of earth. She heard the burble of flowing water, feeling it cool upon her skin.

Stepping out of the hole, she saw her first footprint, and felt known by the world.

Bending her knees, she squatted down in the shade of the great tree to help all the others up into the bright world.

"First -man -of -all -men!" Mantis called. "! Come!"

The first man-of-all-men heard himself named, and climbed up through the dark soil. First woman reached for him and pulled him up into the air of the world.

He looked all around him and saw an immense veld. Sand swirled in the wind, blowing about and about and about.

He was astonished by the blue sky above, and he heard the sun ringing. He saw the mountains and hills, dunes and plains. As his first footprints made a mark upon the earth, he felt known by the world.

"Men- and- women -of -the- first- people!" called Mantis, "! Come!"

And they came, at first in twos and threes and then in a great crowd.

Making their first footprints upon the earth, they smelled the wind and listened to the sun ring.

They felt the warmth of the air and they gazed at the far mountains.

Then they greeted the first man and the first woman in the shade of the great tree and squatted down alongside them.

Mantis stood in the center of his creation, and he called forth the animals by their names.

"Hartebeest!" he called, "! Come!" And Hartebeest scrambled up into the world.

"Porcupine! Blue Crane! Mongoose! Eland! Ostrich! Rhinoceros! Rock-Rabbit! Snake! Elephant! Giraffe! Hyena! Come!"

The animals and the insects and the birds came, the large ones and the small. Two by two they hauled themselves up from under the earth. They were in such a hurry that some crowded up through the trunk of the great tree. They crawled over the branches and dangled like ripe fruit until they dropped onto the ground, joining their brothers and sisters in the shade of the tree.

All greeted each other in their excited click-talk—for in those days the people and the animals were all of one family and spoke the same language.

When the last of the animals had arrived and all were gathered beneath the great tree, Mantis spoke to the shining sun.

"Sun!" he called out, "you are to move across the earth and to hide beneath the earth when you reach the end of the sky. That will make for day and for night."

The bright and ringing sun began slowly to move across the sky.

"Grandmother stars!" called Mantis, "you are to appear when the sun is hiding, and to disappear when the sun returns."

The Grandmothers twinkled in assent.

Mantis plucked a feather from Ostrich's rump, and flung it high in the sky. This made Ostrich take off at a run.

"You, feather, are to lie up in the sky and be the moon when the Grandmothers are there. You are to grow and shrink and to lighten the darkness for the people."

He then went looking for Ostrich, for it was Ostrich who secretly kept fire in the armpit of his wing.

"Oh, Ostrich!" called Mantis. "Oh, Ostrich, I have a treat for you!"

When he found Ostrich behind a bush, furtively tucking his fire out of sight in his wingpit, he said, "If you come with me, I'll take you to a tree with the sweetest yellow plums in the world." Ostrich's mouth watered for those plums, and he greedily followed Mantis to the tree.

"The best ones are high up," Mantis told him when they got there. "No, they're higher still," he said when Ostrich reached for the middle branches.

Ostrich spread his wings to taste the sweetest plums high up, and at that moment Mantis grabbed a flick of the fire and ran back with it to the people.

"You now have three lights," he told the people. "The sun and the moon and fire. The sun will light your days, the moon will light your nights, and fire shall be your hearth in this immense world, keeping you warm and cooking your food. And by its flames, you will be at home wherever you are."

Plucking some dry grass and small tinder from the ground, he showed the people how to make a small flame and then a larger one. Soon crackling flames spit hot, orange light into the air and the people gathered round it, entranced.

The animals were afraid and backed off from the fire. Some hopped under bushes, some ran towards the hills, and others burrowed underground.

And never again could they speak the same language with the people.

But the women -of- the- first- people were grateful for the fire and for the wonder and the beauty of the earth, and began to chant their thanks.

Singing in clear and melodious voices, they swayed and stamped their feet, dancing with arms outstretched. The men joined them, pounding the ground with their feet and clapping with half-cupped hands, making glad with the women. And all inscribed the earth with the footprints of their first dance.

"I have brought you to the upper world to learn how to use it and each other well," spoke Mantis. "Be good to one another and to the children who will follow. Live well, love well, and laugh well."

And he placed his forelegs in prayer position.

"I am tired from my labors," he said. "It is time for me to go to the great water. But, like the moon, I will come back renewed."

Mantis climbed onto the back of Bee, and together they flew far out over the great water. In the middle of the water was a creamy white flower and Bee, by this time quite ready to let go of his burden, lay Mantis down into the center of the great, open blossom, where he promptly fell into a deep, renewing sleep.

First Mother
Wabenaki Peoples

Before there was a world, there was She-Who-Empowers. From the thoughts of her mind would come All of Creation—the Earth and the plants, the creatures and Light. And within her All of Creation would always exist.

She breathed in, and that breath ticked the first moment of Time. She breathed out and her voice sent a rhythmic chant into the darkness:

Hey hey o hey-yo.

She wished for a world with each chant:

Hey hey o hey-yo, and her song swirled and swirled through the emptiness until a round earth appeared.

The Sky came into being, and with it the Sun, and the Moon.

Hey hey o hey-yo.

Seven times she chanted it, and with each chant one of the Seven Brothers, appeared. Like seven sounds, each thundering on a different pitch, they circled the earth as unseen as mist, hovering, waiting.

For they would be the invisible builders of the world.

The Earth was there, and the air, but life did not yet exist. She-Who-Empowers gazed down upon the round, empty planet and released the bits of dust left over from the shaping of the Earth, letting them sift into a mound at the edge of the Land.

Hey hey o hey-yo, she chanted. The dirt began to bulge this way and that, shaking up and down until a black-haired, featureless god emerged.

He pulled his shoulders out of the ground and his arms, then his chest and his hips. His legs remained rooted.

He-Who-Makes-Himself-From-Something appeared in the world.

Hey hey o hey-yo. With a bolt of lightning, She-Who-Empowers gave him an eye.

Hey hey o hey-yo. A second bolt created his other eye. Seven strikes of lightning gave him two eyes, two ears and two nostrils—but only one mouth. That was so he would listen twice as much as he would talk.

"This is good!" said She-Who-Empowers. "For so long I have heard the whisper of your coming. For you are the ancestor of generations yet to be born. You are the Transformer, the one from whom all change shall come. Everything is good."

He -Who-Makes-Himself-From-Something smiled and immediately set to work changing the shape of the earth. With strong fingers he scooped out basins for the oceans and lakes, and gouged out channels for the mighty rivers. He piled rocks and soil into hills and mountains, and he blew clouds into the sky to bring rain.

Impatient to move farther afield, he pulled his legs out of the earth, first one and then the other. He wriggled his toes and flexed his knees to get the cricks out, and then strode out across the Land to bring forth sweet grasses and trees—birch and maple, beech and the stately ash.

The green world appeared, covering hills and rolling plains. It was beautiful and he was well pleased, but he wished to make one last masterpiece—a long, sparkling lake—and with a sweep of both arms he created the Water-Between-the-Lands.

The lake enchanted him so much that he sat down upon its shore to admire his handiwork, and stayed there through many seasons of ice and many seasons of fragrant breezes until, at last, he began to feel lonely. It was time for him to bring into being the creatures—the animal people and the human people—for whom the world had been made.

Picking up his drum he drummed the creatures, one by one, into existence. He made White Bear, his animal helper, and Wind Eagle, who made the winds to blow. He made the rabbits and the deer, the porcupines and the wolves. He made elk and moose and salmon and beaver. He made the Close-to-the-Earth people—the snakes and toads and newts—and he made the birds to fly in the air. He even put pesky mosquitoes in his world—but also, butterflies.

The world was finally complete with everything the humans would need for food and clothing and shelter. He-Who-Made-Himself-From-Something longed to hear the voices of people, and to hear his own voice speaking to them, as well. But first, not knowing how the animal people might react to the human people, he decided to put the animals to a test.

He drew in a deep breath. Clearing his throat and preparing his lips to speak his first word he cried, "human people!". His own voice was startling in his ears, but with his first word his name changed from He-Who-Made-Himself-from-Something to He-Who-Speaks.

The deer leaped away, and the elk and the rabbits. They fled into the forest, hiding in the brush.

"Uh-hunh!" said He-Who-Speaks. "This is good. The humans will have to hunt them for food, and the ones who escape will be able to reproduce their own kind."

He cried the word for humans again. The bears growled and shambled off into the woods, the wolves and foxes bounding after them, barking loudly and showing their fangs.

"Uh-hunh!" he said. "This is good because the humans shall fear them and treat them with respect."

He turned his attention to the moose and the squirrels as he called one more time. The squirrels and the moose were *gigantic*—as tall as the tallest tree—and extremely moody. He had no idea how they might react to humans.

"Chi-chi-chi-chi!" shrieked the enormous squirrel with an ear-splitting clamor. It raced about wildly, tearing up the forest and swatting He-Who-Speaks with its mighty bush of a tail.

"Snort-snort-snort-snort!" boomed the moose, butting its great, antlered head against trees, crashing about and kicking up tree roots and huge clods of mud.

"Uh-oh!" said He-Who-Speaks. "This is not good. They will cause great distress to the people. What shall I do with these two creatures? I'll have to make them smaller, that's for sure."

He chased the gigantic squirrel through the brush, finally catching it by its tail and sitting on it, patting its sides soothingly until the squirrel shrank into a tiny, scampering thing and took off into the treetops, chattering and complaining to its heart's content. It was still a rambunctious creature, but was now too small to be harmful to humans.

Then he followed the trail of the moose—which cut a very broad swath through the woods—and when he caught up with it, pressed his palm hard against the moose's forehead. As he pushed, it's face became smaller and smaller until its head was only as large as a whole pig—but no longer as large as a whole horse. And he sent the moose deep into the wilds of the woods.

Food was now plentiful, the waterways were good for paddling and the pure air was fragrant for breathing. The world was ready for humans. He-Who-Speaks gathered stones and red earth, and began to shape the First Mother. He placed her head to the North and her feet to the South, spreading out her arms East and West. Then he leaned over her body and breathed into her mouth to awaken her into life. She sat up, blinking, and looked around. He smiled welcomingly at his creation, but she didn't smile back at him. Stiffly, she got to her feet and took a few hesitant steps before finding her stride and setting out to see her world. She never even looked back.

He-Who-Speaks felt even more lonely than before. The First Mother was handsome, it was true, and she was strong and well made, but she had no fire of life in her eyes. He wasn't sure what to do.

"Come back!" he finally cried out after her. She turned around and came back to him without expression while he regarded her critically, not quite pleased with what he had made. She understood right away, and said,

"It is because I'm too hard. I have no heart. Make me again, but this time use a living tree, for the dew falls on the leaf and the sun warms the dew—and that warmth is life. Make me of the tree and I shall be that life."

So he took apart her stony body and scattered the pieces far and wide. Then he walked into the forest and searched for the right tree with which to fashion the First Mother. When he saw the ash, tall and slender and dancing gracefully in the wind, he knew he had found the perfect one. Gently stripping off its bark, he smoothed and sculpted the trunk into a beautiful, silky woman. Its branches became her shining black braid, and its roots became her strong, agile feet.

She was warm and juicy with sap, her green heart pulsing with feeling. Stepping out of the living wood, she breathed in with rapture the green fragrance of the forest, and breathed out to the whole world her power. Seeing He-Who-Speaks gazing in wonder at her, she threw back her head and laughed delightedly into the air.

"Oh, such beauty everywhere!" she exclaimed. "Who shall be my partner to share this with? Shall I choose from amongst the Seven Brothers," she teased. From out of the mists they immediately drifted, each presenting himself with bolts of lightning and great claps of thunder, each trying hard to impress her. He-Who-Speaks waited, and when the sound and fury had died down, spoke to her softly, his eyes on fire with love.

" I see you, and I see the goodness of your woman's heart." he said. Holding out her hand to him, as they both knew she would, she greeted He-Who-Speaks and took him as the First Father.

Through many springtimes they lived together in shared peace and comfort, begetting generation after generation of children. But far in the North lived the Guardians of Winter, the Ice Giants, who were so jealous of First Father's good fortune

that they caused the winds to blow so cold and so harsh that Winter never ended; Spring never came. The Earth which fed the grass never thawed and the grass which fed the deer never grew. The deer which fed the people sickened and died, and the people who fed on the deer began to starve. The famine was so severe that all the living things—the plants and the animals and the people—were dying.

First Mother watched her children slowly sicken, and with the sight that dwelt behind her eyes she saw that there was only one thing that would save her children.

She whispered to her husband, "If you love me and wish to make me happy, you must take away my life so that all my children may live. For the substance of the Mother must cycle—live and die in order to be reborn, so the world may live in balance."

For several heartbeats First Father was silent, but with his deep sight that dwelt behind his eyes, he knew that she was right. Only her self-sacrifice would help to heal the world. With a sorrowing heart he did as she asked him to do. When the children were not looking, he sacrificed her, gazing at the night sky as she climbed the white mountain and stepped upon the trail of stars.

He whispered after her. "Travel well."

When she was dead, he grabbed her by the hank of her black hair and dragged her body across the cold ground, just as she had asked him to do. He dragged her over snow-covered stones and jagged dry sticks; he dragged her over frosted hummocks of spiny grass and across needle-sharp shards of ice. He dragged her until all the flesh of her body had been rubbed off, and when there was nothing left of her but bones, he buried the bones in the frozen, hard earth.

"Leave my bones to moulder for seven months," she had told him. "After that, come back with my children and my children's children, and feast upon the corn plants you find growing there. Then set aside a portion of the corn for seed, and plant the seeds in the ground for next year's harvest."

First Father and the children did exactly as she had instructed, and they held a feast, eating the sacred corn that the First Mother had provided with her sacrifice. Then they dug up her bones, made a great fire and sat around it, singing songs of praise to her, and thanksgiving. And as they watched the smoke spiral up into the night sky, they sent their prayers with it—prayers for their Mother, for themselves and for all their relations.

So that is a story of the peoples who live in the Northeast woodlands of the American continent, whose mother was born of the ash tree and whose power is always felt everywhere. For it is her flesh that feeds us, and it is the smoke of her fiery body that moves our hearts and our minds. It is from the goodness of a woman's heart that we receive the daily blessing of life: this is what we must remember when we eat of her substance and when our hearts are full with her goodness.

For we are all relations of the First Mother—
all of us—and it is through sharing with each
other that her love for us shall be fulfilled.

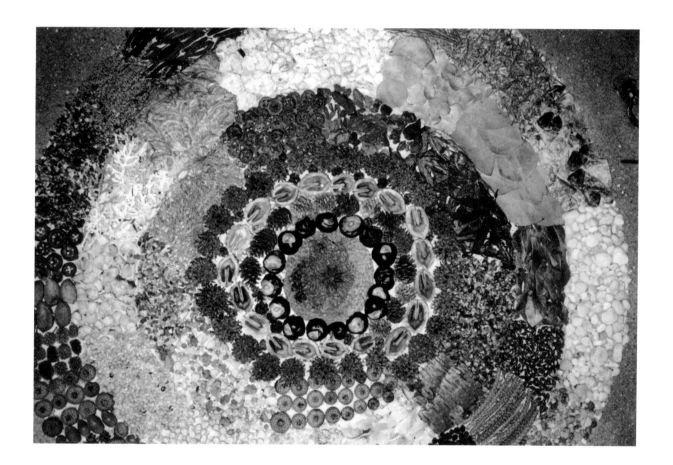

Eurynome and Ophion
Pre-Hellenic Greece

*B*efore there was anything else, there was Eternity. Like a primeval sea, Eternity was fathomless and empty—a Source. But the Source held something—a dream, a breath of desire.

Breathing out, the Source shook the silent stillness into a chaos of sound, singing into Eternity its dream for a world.

From the song a Goddess slowly materialized—Eurynome, the Wide-Wanderer. It was in her body that the very nature of Being would reside. Euronyme, who would be here and everywhere as long as the song was sung; Euronyme through whom whole worlds might be born.

She took form and appeared, naked and alone, upon the empty waters.

Hearing the Source's song of longing, she began to dance, and from her motion Space and Time were created. Her first movement was to separate the Sky from the waters and she lifted her arms, bent her knees to steady herself, and pushed hard. Slowly the sky lifted, creating space around her. She stamped and twirled, flicking crests of foam with her feet, and danced lonely upon the waves.

She spun towards the South, the ripples of her movements echoing out behind her. The very air was set into motion, swirling all around her in whirlpools of wind. The North Wind, newly arisen at her back, played with her, chasing between her legs and blowing into her armpits. She teased it in turn, leaping towards the wind and away, feeling it with her face, her arms, her torso.

"Ahhh!" she sang, her own song resonating through layers of new-formed clouds, "How I yearn for a companion!"

The Source dreamed and watched; watched and dreamed until the winds, of themselves, gathered in response to her call, streaming and pulsing. Eurynome caught a strand of the North Wind and felt for its rhythm, swaying to its beat and molding it with her hands, rolling it and rubbing it until it began to accrete girth, take form and grow.

Listening for the pattern that had first created her, Eurynome shaped from the North Wind a being as vital as she—the Prodigious Serpent Ophion.

She flung out her arms to this creature she had made, cold and shivering with her efforts. Irresistibly drawn, he undulated through the mists towards her, wrapping the end of his tail hesitantly around her knees before coiling seven times around her body.

The shock of his first caress did nothing to warm her, and she spun around faster inside his embrace to generate heat. Ophion tightened his hold and Eurynome gasped. Thus entwined, they whirled more and more wildly upon the waves, diving and circling, twisting and thrusting until their limbs were hot and the waters churned with foam. Ophion coiled more tightly, squeezing, their song rising higher and their dance more frenzied as Eurynome, shuddering with a cry that rent the new air, opened and took the Serpent Ophion into herself.

Fertilized by the North Wind, the Wide-Wandering Goddess softened, grew heavy and sank down to brood upon the waves. She shape-shifted gradually into a dove, pure gray and feathery, letting the watery currents support her while the child she carried, grew.

Languidly swimming nearby, Ophion watched and waited until the day his consort/mother tucked in her wings, growled deep in her throat and labored to bring forth an egg—the wondrous Universal Egg.

From the One had Eurynome been created—making Two. From the Two was Ophion created, making Three—and from this trinity was born the Universal Egg from which the multitudes would arise.

Eurynome relaxed. Now it was Ophion's turn to brood. Just as he had coiled around the mother, he now spiraled seven times around their progeny, protecting the Egg well. Bobbing gently upon the waves they waited and rested; rested and waited. Then one day Ophion pressed the shell more tightly, and the Egg began to hatch.

At first there was just a crack, but then the Egg opened, split into two halves and out tumbled Eros, their first child—the God of Love.

The baby Eros was male and female—both! Eros was born with great golden wings, four heads and came out roaring like a bull, bleating like a ram, and hissing like a snake. This child, it seemed, could do anything!

Eros' birth signified that all things in the world would now be brought forth from Love.

Eros looked up at the sky and the Sun and the Moon were created. Then the stars and planets and galaxies appeared. Earth came next, and Eros playfully made it to sink here and buckle there, causing lakes to form, and mountains and plains and rolling hills. Rivers meandered through lush green valleys and trees sprang onto the edges of fertile plains. A multitude of plants put out seed, and the first creatures hopped and ran and flew, filling the air with their calls.

When the Sun slipped lingeringly behind the hills, darkness quieted the land, and when the Moon did the same, the night dissolved into a birdsong dawn.

All of this Eros made. Poking a finger into the rich soil, Eros tried to coax forth a human being, but without success.

"Try this," suggested Ophion, yanking two teeth from his mouth and placing them on the ground. Eros planted the two teeth, and from them sprang the first people, the Pelasgians.

Now that there was solid land to walk upon, Eurynome and Ophion, leaving their child below, turned to climb to the top of the highest mountain—Mount Olympus—from where they might watch over their whole Creation.

There they lived peacefully through many generations. The world that had been made through Love was beautiful. Forests breathed in great green breaths, and the fields were golden with ripened grain. Vines hung heavy with purple clusters of grapes, and the lambs sucked lustily at their mothers' teats.

Gazing out over the sea one evening, watching the play of golden light dapple the water in a dazzling path from the setting sun, Ophion remarked in a self-satisfied voice, "Quite a fine kingdom I have made for you, if I must say so myself!"

"*You* have made?" Eurynome challenged him sharply, appalled at his arrogance.

"Of course I have made," he repeated, daring her to contradict him. "I am the Father, am I not?" She stared at him, disbelieving.

"Have you forgotten already?" she complained. In her mind's ear she could hear the song that had sung her into being, and see the dance upon the waves that had drawn

Ophion forth from the winds. She stamped her foot in anger while he rose defiantly to his full height, bullying her.

She became so enraged that she kicked him hard, bruising his head with the heel of her foot and knocking out all his teeth. He tried to fight back, to protect his face from her blows, but she pummeled him mercilessly and then pushed him to the edge of Mount Olympus and shoved him off.

"Go back to the dark caves under the earth!" she shrieked. "You are banished from here!" She was sobbing in her fury and disappointment. "Who do you think made *you*?"

Alone again, hurting and lonely, she gazed up at the night sky their child had made. Planets floated amongst the stars.

"Wanderers, like myself," she whispered. She greeted them, each according to its own particular quality, naming each one and assigning each its task in the world.

"Sun!" she called to the one that would show itself again at dawn. "Your task is to illuminate the world. Help us to see clearly!"

To the Moon she called, "Moon, you are the enchantress. Show us the way to mystery."

"Mars," she called, "You are to govern growth of all things that live, each in its own way, each in its own scale of time."

"From you, Mercury, we ask for wisdom and for the understanding that knowledge is *not* the same thing as wisdom."

"We count on you, Jupiter, to help us to make just laws and maintain them fairly."

"Venus, O my Venus, help us learn how to love."

"And from you, Saturn, we ask to be shown the way to peace. Teach us, please."

Standing in the dark, alone at the top of Mount Olympus, she listened for the song that had once sung her into being. Hearing the wash of sound coming from the myriad stars studding the night sky, she swayed to its rhythm, humming with it and dancing in soft, small steps.

But her heart was heavy for she knew—as women know these things—that soon enough the peace of this place would be rudely threatened by hordes of squabbling Gods who would storm the mountain, crowding out the silence. They would be the new Olympians, rough and bloodthirsty, whose dance would be danced with clashing swords and whose songs would ring loud with deceit and cunning.

And she knew—as women know these things—that they would know little of how to listen for the sounds of that first song—the song that had brought their world into being.

Iznami and Iznagi

Japan

In the beginning, long before Heaven and Earth even existed, there was Chaos. Like a raw egg without a shell, it rolled around in "no-where", liquid and slimy and filled with the potential for life.

The egg-whites, light and clear, were the first to lift from the Chaos and disperse high up to create the masculine Yo, Heaven. The rich, heavy yolk—much more complicated—sank later, spreading and hardening to become the feminine Io, Earth.

From Io and Yo came seven generations of male Deities, the No-Mikoto, and for the eighth generation they created Iznagi and Iznami, the Receptive Couple—
the Ones Who Invite.

Iznagi and Iznami, yearning for the Earth, stood on the floating bridge of Heaven and peered down at the primeval waters below.

"Hai!" they called, listening for a response. But the Earth was silent.

Reaching for the Jewelled Spear of Heaven, Iznagi thrust it through the clouds until it reached the watery realm and then he plunged it deep into the waves. He felt the drag of the running sea, and as he pulled the spear out, a great drop of brine fell back onto the water, congealing as it fell. And so was the first island, Ono-goro-jima, born.

Planting the spear into the new land, Iznagi and Iznami, the first ancestors, slid down the pillar from Heaven to stand upon the soil of the world.

"You will be my wife and I will be your husband," declared Iznagi.

"You will be my husband, and I will be your wife," responded Iznami. And so they walked around the pillar of the world, he to the left and she to the right.

"Hai!" Iznami exclaimed when they met, "what a handsome fellow you are!" But Iznagi stamped his foot in anger.

"I am the man, and I'm supposed to say that first! Otherwise it's unlucky. Let's start over."

Iznami folded her hands demurely in front of her, bowing her head to hide a tiny smile, and walked again around the pillar, her toes pointed modestly inward. This time when they met, Iznagi said loudly,

"Hai! What a lovely woman you are!" And they both bowed. He gazed at her up and down, from her long, black tresses to her dainty feet, as if he were seeing her for the first time. "Tell me, how is your body formed?"

"Why, it is quite perfect," she murmured, running her hands suggestively over her breasts and hips. "There is just one small space in it that still needs to be filled. And how is your body formed?"

Iznagi pulled his shoulders back, and flexing his biceps declared, "My loins are powerful and my legs well muscled. But I have just the extra appendage that would be honored to fill your space."

"I invite you to come," whispered Iznami huskily. Irresistibly they moved towards each other and by the pillar of the world they became husband and wife.

Their offspring were many, and beautiful. Their firstborns became the eight islands dotting the Sea of Japan; they gave birth to mountains and rivers and waterfalls, mists and forests and fields. Their children were the ancestors of trees and of plants, of birds and fish and of all the creatures.

When Iznagi washed his eyes in the clear waters of a flowing stream, the Sun was born, and the Moon.

And when their first human child—Oho-hiro-me, Great Noon—was born, so radiant was she that they lifted her up to Heaven as Sun-helper. Then they made the wind to blow away the mists from the land, allowing the Sun to illuminate the six corners of the world—North, South, East, West, Above and Below.

The helper of the Moon was born next. Glowing almost as brightly as his sister, he was sent to meet her in Heaven where, each night, his task was to reflect her light.

Their next child—Hiruku the Leech Child—was born defective. For three years they tried to teach him to stand, but failing, they bundled him into a tiny camphor-wood boat and set him adrift, letting the winds take him.

Next came Sosa-no-wa, the terror of the family. He screamed, he wailed, he destroyed everything he could get his hands on. Whole forests withered at his touch, animals fled from him in terror. The clamor was deafening, and his exasperated parents finally sent him down to Hell where he belonged.

"Please," said Iznami, exhausted by the travails of her last two children, "I'd like to have some gentler offspring to watch over the Elements."

So she conceived triplets. The Goddess of Water and the Goddess of Earth were born first and while suckling them, one on each nipple, she felt her belly ripple with the heat of their womb-twin, the God of Fire.

"Aieyy!" she cried in searing pain, lying down again to deliver this burning burden of a child. But consuming her flesh with the flames of his being, the God of Fire killed his mother in the roar of his birth.

Once born, his mother dead, he moved quickly. Covering his sister, the Goddess of Earth, Waka-musubi was conceived. The spirit of young growth, she was born with the silkworm and mulberry tree growing out of the crown of her head; from her navel sprouted the five sacred grains.

"Whatever you do, don't look back," warned Iznami, as she saw him pull the comb out of his hair and break off one of its teeth. He lit it like a candle, and she cried, "Don't…!" as he turned suddenly to behold her in its small flame seeing, instead of his beloved Iznami, a burnt, decaying corpse half-eaten by maggots. Horrified, he turned and fled from his dead wife who followed him in hot pursuit.

"Catch him!" Iznami shrieked, calling forth all the Demons and Furies of the Underworld to help her. "Make him stay here with me!"

Iznagi, in his terror, tried to escape from the wailing Furies pursuing him, running faster and flinging in their path the teeth from his comb—which they mistook for bamboo shoots—and the ornaments, which they mistook for grapes and plums. Stooping to grab and eat the false fruits slowed them down just enough so that he reached the opening to the Underworld just in time to scramble out safely.

Iznagi missed his wife keenly, and after a time went to seek her in the Land of the Dead, Yomi's realm, in order to bring her back. He dressed in his finest robes and tied his hair back with her favorite comb, which was shaped like ornamental fruit.

When he arrived in Yomi's gloomy land, Iznami greeted him with relief, chiding,

"You took your time coming. I've already consumed Yomi's cooking, but lead me out of here, and I'll follow you." He searched for her in the darkness, but although he heard her voice, he could not see her. "Just start walking," she cried impatiently, "but whatever you do, don't look back!"

That made Iznagi want to see her all the more, but he started walking back towards the opening of the pit, hearing the rustle of his wife's presence behind him.

But Iznami was right behind him. She grabbed onto a branch of a peach tree just on the lit side of the opening, and was hauling herself back into the World when Iznagi, plucking three ripe peaches from the tree, threw them back into the pit at her. Wildly she reached for them, and in that moment

Iznagi took his chance, and rolled a massive rock over the opening, creating a boundary between the Land of Yomi from the Land of the Living forever.

"Aiyee!" raged Iznami. "I will get back at you! From now on, I will cause one thousand people to die every day!"

"And I," called Iznagi through the stone, "will cause fifteen-hundred people to be born every day, so that death will never catch up with life!"

Iznami cried, disconsolate, while Iznagi hung his head and listened to his wife's heartrending sobs. When they became gulps and weak shudders, he said sadly, "It is over. You can come this far, but no farther. We are separated." And making a long, deep bow to the rock, he slowly removed his robe and his sash, his slippers and his pants, letting go of the defilement of death and disease, piece by piece.

Then he walked to the flowing waters of the clear stream and performed his ablutions, ducking his head under and rising to blow prayers to the winds. With each submersion, he blew the rest of the Deities of Heaven and Earth and Sea into being, completing the task of Creation.

He made:

Iha-tsu-tsu-no-Mikato

Oho-hano-bi-no-Kami

Sokotsu-tsu-no-Mikato

Oho-aya-tsu-bi-no-Kami

Aka-tsu-tsu-no-Mikato

It was done. As the Sun set in the sky and the Moon rose, he made his silent way to the island of Ahaji.

And there he dwelt for the rest of time, a hermit, in meditation and prayer.

1. The Hymn of Creation
Rig Veda ~ India

In the beginning, before there was Anything
   At All,
What was there?
Before there was even Nothing At All,
what was there?
And where was it?
Before there was day or night, birth or death
Could there have been some knowing, invisible
   Spirit,
Some essence of goodness,
like a conscious, infinite Presence
breathing with windless breath?
In this darkness shrouded by darkness,
In this fathomless ocean of featureless, still water,
Could this unmoving force have caught its breath
   with longing
and roiled the dark waters into hot motion,
Planting the primal seed—born of desire—
Into the heated Void?

Those poets who seek to understand,
gather that Being arises from Non-Being,
as if a subtle cord were stretched
between what is above and whatever is below.
The seed, then, sowed in Spirit
Would take its root in Matter.
But who really knows, who can say for sure
how the world first came to be?
Even the gods themselves came later,
arising, as they did, from the primal seed.
But of that first spark of desire—the one that
started all creation—we can only make a guess.
If there is an ultimate Spirit,
An all-encompassing intelligence
that permeates the whole of existence, then
   perhaps
that Knower knows how it all happened.
But maybe not…

2. The Legend of Creation
Rig Veda ~ India

The primal seed floated in the fathomless sea. For one thousand years it slept, embraced by the warm, generative waters until it grew into a golden, cosmic egg.

And then a wind blew, agitating the waters and cleaving the golden egg in two. Like an embryo giving birth to life-fire, the golden egg split apart and the Lord Prajapati, who was Brahman, burst full grown out of the center. His body was hard as a rock, his face large and round and the eggshell, falling on either side of him, was half silver and half gold.

And beholding the opposite shore of his own life, he saw that he would live for one thousand years.

Prajapati, the Lord of Progeny, was made of mortal flesh and hair, bone and marrow. But behind this body was an immortal spirit: the ear of the ear, the eye of the eye, the word of words, the mind of mind, and the life of life.

Looking down upon the waters with power he saw his own moving reflection, and his heart beat with love. For a full year he gazed rapt at his image shadowed in the water, yearning to create a world from himself. And then, as any child will by the age of one year, he spoke his first words: the sacred sounds that brought the world into being.

"*Bhuh!*" he called, his voice ringing into the moist darkness over the waters.

And the Earth appeared.

"*Bhuvah!*" he called, his sounds echoing in all directions and fading out beyond hearing.

And the Air sprang into existence.

"*Svah!*" he sang with all his force, creating howling winds that blew upwards and outwards.

And the Sky spread above and out into unseeable space.

Five syllables he had pronounced, and they became the five seasons.

It was begun! Singing praises, the wind from his breath whipped the water into crests of foam which, lifting and tumbling, became the dancing gods of the Cosmos.

With heads of foam and churning feet they rose from the generative sea, arms legs and torsos ever-changing, joyously dancing.

But they swirled and leapt in darkness and, longing for light, Prajapati skimmed a bit of foam off their heads, tossed it up into the Sky and created the Sun!

The steady gaze of the Sun, like a single point of desire bestowing its gifts, illuminated Earth and Waters, Air and Sky into life and color! It dappled the waves and lifted the winds. It spun the Earth and sent clouds scudding over the Gods' dance.

Now that the world was lit, Prajapati grew hot with the desire for company. Dividing himself in half, he created his female counterpart. Joining, they co-created all living things into being.

Imagining plants and breathing out, they caused the plants to spring into life.

Visualizing winged creatures in the air, they created birds in flight.

They blinked and from their eyes came horses and four-footed beasts. They listened and from their hearing sheep appeared, and cows. They called and from their voices came goats, bleating. *Bh-aaa! Bh-aaa!*

And then from the deep longing in their souls they imagined others in their same form—and they created humankind.

They went wild with creative activity!

They made snakes to slither through the grasses and they made striped tigers, to pounce. They made lotus flowers to float upon the waters and peacocks to shimmer iridescent tail-feathers. They created elephants and lizards, banyan trees and mangos. They made buzzing insects and night-blooming jasmine—and humans to dream of wonders.

The world was full, and the company was great!

The Lords of Progeny stood back to watch their creation flourish, but soon everything began mysteriously to die. One by one, species by species they languished, fell down and disintegrated back into thin air.

Alarmed, Prajapati assumed the shape of a tortoise and crawled slowly over the earth to see what had happened.

And discovered, to his dismay, that they had forgotten to provide *food* for their creation!

So they began all over again, re-creating the birds and the fishes, the beasts and the people, the trees and the insects.

This time, however, they provided their creatures with full udders and teats, great nipples and breasts teeming with milk.

And the creatures drank. The plants drank from the earth and rain and sun; the fishes drank from the waters of the sea. And from the milk that flowed freely from the mothers of all beings, the new creatures took the milky nourishment into themselves for sustenance, and lived!

The Feathered Serpent

Quiche Maya

Waters shushing and lapping in sighing silence, the emptiness dark and still. There is no earth, no person, no rock, no canyon, forest, no hill. No animal, no tree, no bird, fish, crab. Only sea beneath all the sky, waiting, still, silent. Only sibilant ripples of whispering waters in the dark, in the night, murmuring. *Sshh-shss.*

Only a glitter of sound, a whisper of light is there, hidden in the waters. Only the double spirit of Knowing and Begetting sparks the silent darkness. It is Tepeu/Gucumatz, the mother/father, the creator/modeler, the blue-green bird/snake that is the Great Feathered Serpent in its two aspects.

These Two-Makers-in-a-Single-Being, this mother/father glittering with the life-force that would make a world, had a longing to imagine and bring into existence Form from the void. They started thinking, and the stillness stirred into motion, the sweeping wind of their thinking becoming the first sacred Word, the first prayer to count the world into existence.

"Earth!" cried the Feathered Serpent, awakening the Heart of Earth as the word echoed over the waters. And the first layer, the hard bones of the world, were revealed from beneath the mist-covered waters. Mountains of stone and fire thrust from the sea as the repeated word—Earth… Earth… Earth… earth… earth…echoed into eternity.

All-the-Sky made place for the Earth, lifting above the rocks and waters until it had found its spreading space, and the very Heart of Sky was awakened into being.

Thinking green thoughts—the growth of stem and leaf and vine—the Feathered Serpent spoke the word "Plants!" The sound was cast, sown like a scattering of seed onto the new earth. And the earth received the seed and gradually dawned with green growth. Trees and grass covered the highlands and the lowlands. Flowering vines and fruiting seed pods sprouted, spiraling, and tasseled stalks of kernelled corn grew straight and golden.

This was the second layer of the world.

The sea was there, and the green-fleshed land, but not the flowing, sprinkling, gushing wetness that would sustain the roots and branches.

"Water!" cried the Feathered Serpent, mother/father of the world. The father imagined the torrential thrusts of cataract and storm, and brought them into being. The mother reflected the mirroring lakes and placid pools, and brought them into being.

From the Heart of Sky came three flashes of lightning—Hurricane, Newborn Thunderbolt and Sudden Thunderbolt— and dark clouds gathered, thunder crashing and the rains streamed and poured and coursed onto the land. The earth soaked up the rain and let the runoff tumble down towards the sea.

The third layer of existence came into being.

The Great Feathered Serpent imagined those who would inhabit the river valleys and plains, the mountains and air and the waters. They thought of runners and leapers, of winged ones and crawlers. They imagined scaly hides and furred haunches, feathers and pelt and shell.

They called, "Breathing ones!"

In the canyons and thickets appeared the deer and the puma and the jaguar. Rattlesnakes coiled beneath the bushes and birds tucked their nests in high trees. Running, snorting, calling, panting, the animals rustled through the grasses every which way, making a great swish of sound.

Hearing all the squawking and chattering, the Makers wondered,

"What is all this meaningless noise? Why don't you speak to one another, each in your own language? Why don't you thank us, your Makers and the Source of your being, for all that has been given you? Call us like this:

Heart of Sky, Heart of Earth, Mother/Father, Tepeu/Gucumatz the Great Feathered Serpent in two aspects, we call you by your name just as you have created us by naming us!"

But the creatures could only bark and whimper and growl. They could not praise their Makers. They could not count the days of the world.

The Feathered Serpent thought further, and then spoke.

"You may remain where you are, in the canyons and the fields. Whatever has been given you on the earth, you may keep. But you must accept that you are here to serve, as your animal flesh shall be food for the human creatures still to come. You shall feed them, the Fruit of the Earth. By your dying, they shall live."

And so the fourth layer of the world came into being.

As a tree puts down roots into the soil and grows upwards towards the light before branching out with leaves and fruit, so was each layer of the world planted in the Source of all Being. Layer by layer it accreted substance and attributes until the world was ready for its Fruit—the fifth layer of the human ones.

The humans would taste and smell and laugh and learn, honoring their Makers by remembering them and enjoying the deliciousness of the world in all its forms.

"It is almost time for the Dawning of the World," the Feathered Serpent thought. "The ground is prepared, and now we must sow the seeds that will cause the humans to appear over the rim of the world. These will be the ones who will know how to taste

the colors of the dawn and love the spirits and bodies of each other. These shall be the people who will remember where they came from and will know to give thanks.

Scooping up some mud from the earth, the mother/father fashioned a single human being, molding its head and arms and legs, patting extra blobs of mud on the belly and the buttocks. Standing back to admire their handiwork, they saw that the face was lopsided and the eyes blank and unclear. The figure tried to walk, but first it lost a foot and then one arm crumbled and fell off, and the belly-blob sagged. The human being fell apart as it dried until it was nothing but a pile of dirt on the ground.

"Hmmm-nm," said the Makers. "Earth is not enough. We must try again with something from the plant layer of creation as the Dawning is drawing closer."

They invoked the help of Grandmother of Day and the Grandfather—the ones who separate Time from the Timeless: the counters.

"Please help us design the human ones, the ones who may nurture and provide, and who shall remember their Source! Help us to create the ones who shall long to be loved by their Makers!"

Grandmother and Grandfather spoke.

"You must say their Holy Names, their secret names, their memory sounds to count them into existence. Search the woods for their making—the copal tree for the males and the heart of bulrushes for the females."

And so copal wood was found and carved, and white hearts of bulrushes, and men and women were fashioned to people the earth. These humans had speech, and they walked and multiplied, but they were skinny and brittle and bloodless. Their bodies were dry, their faces crusty. They lurched around, neither laughing nor crying, not singing or dancing or praising their Makers. And the moment of dawning was fast approaching.

The Feathered Serpent, the mother/ father had wished to design humans who spoke eloquently, humans who could both receive the useful wonders of the world and reciprocate with appreciative praise. But these wooden people had no hearts, no fine minds. The Makers were sorely disappointed.

So they called upon Heart of Sky to rain down a sour smelling rain to darken the World and flood the earth. And they called the jaguars to assist them, to bound after the people and tear them open, gouging out their eyes and eating their brittle flesh. Pouncing on their prey, the jaguars growled and dripped saliva, pounding the people's bones to smithereens, crushing their faces and snapping off their heads as they ate.

And still it rained and poured black rain. The world was in cataclysm as all the things the people had used without thanks rose up and attacked them. Their dogs and their turkeys ran after them; their griddles and grinding stones took to the air in fury. Their cooking pots and water jars and hearthstones, in a clanging mayhem, flew every which way, chasing the people up trees and into caves.

Crash! Bam! Clunk! Bang!

Those humans who could still move fled into the forest, scrambling up trees and clinging onto branches to avoid the attacking pots and pans. In fear they chattered like monkeys, their faces crushed, their eyes wide with fright.

And the dawning grew closer.

And closer. The blue-green Feathered Serpent; the mother/father Makers; Tepeu/Gucumatz continued to sing and speak the World into existence, filling it out layer by layer. The sounds and rhythms of each thing being itself filled the Heart of Earth and the Heart of Sky, but the humans had still not been created.

"Mountain Lion!" called the Feathered Serpent. "Coyote! Parrot! Crow!"

The Makers gathered their helpers to begin forming the next human beings.

"Go and gather ears of white corn and yellow corn to make the people. Bring beans as well, and water so that we may grind the food and mix it to make a fragrant paste. And hurry, for the first day will be dawning soon."

Mountain Lion and Coyote and Parrot and Crow ran off, and they brought back sacks of white corn and yellow corn, beans and jars of water to make into a pasty dough which would be the flesh and the blood of the people.

The Makers sang incantations as they shaped the first men out of the food crops, molding them with strong, straight backs and fine, muscled legs. Their heads they made beautiful, with clear-seeing eyes, and their chests were broad and held strong beating hearts. Nine drinks of cornmeal were made, which the men drank, growing still stronger and more comely and wise.

Four men there were—one for each of the Four Directions—and they gazed around them with pleasure at the abundance of food plants surrounding them: honey and cacao, japotes and anonas, jacotes and matasonos.

"It is magnificent and good," they said, using eloquent phrases to honor the blue-green mother/father Makers who had made them. Bowing to the Feathered Serpent, they spoke from their hearts and minds, praising all the layers of the world, seeing high into the Heart of Sky and deep into the Heart of Earth.

Their speech was like poetry, and they praised things hidden, from the tops of high mountains to the depths of great lakes. They saw how all things were connected each to each, were connected to themselves, the first men, as well as to the Source of all Being. They felt in their bodies the turnings of the tides and the cycling of the winds.

They recalled the miracle of their own birth and imagined the females who would come to partner them. Their sight encompassed the whole majesty of the world the Makers had made, and they bowed again in gratitude.

The Dawn was almost upon them, but the Makers were not entirely pleased.

"What do we do now?" they asked each other. "These people are much too perfect—they are too much like us! What if they think they are Gods, and they don't bother to procreate? What if they try and take over our position and cease to be grateful to us? What if they, too, forget where they came from?

But there was little time left. The carrier of Dawn—the lovely Morning Star—was almost at the horizon of the world. What to do? Heart of Sky took in a breath and blew out a mist that covered the eyes of the people, clouding their vision so that they could no longer see the far, hidden things, but could only see clearly what was up close to them. In this way, all the wisdom of the first four men was destroyed, and they would have to work hard to regain what they had lost.

While the first four men slept, the Makers gave them wives. Beautiful shimmering rainbows of women, like clear and sparking water, appeared to lay beside their husbands and conceive the first tribes of the Quiche people—the black and the white, the large and the small, the speakers of many tongues.

When the sky to the East began to show gray and then mauve, and the Morning Star rose to herald the coming of the Dawn, the new people awoke and lit incense for the appearance of the sun. The jaguars awoke and the pumas, the Queletzu bird stretched its wings, as did the eagles and the vultures and the songbirds. And when the first rays of light began to glow upon the horizon, all the beings—animal and human—burst into joyous shouts and roars and cries of welcome. The sun rose warm into the vault of sky, its sun-eyes golden with honey, its light falling upon every corner of the earth at the same time.

Light! Light! Light!

The sound of the sun echoed light into eternity, warming the cold and hardening the shapes and forms of the world so that all could live long lives, with sweet honey in their hearts.

And could say Thank you, Thank you, thank you, thank you… thirteen times.

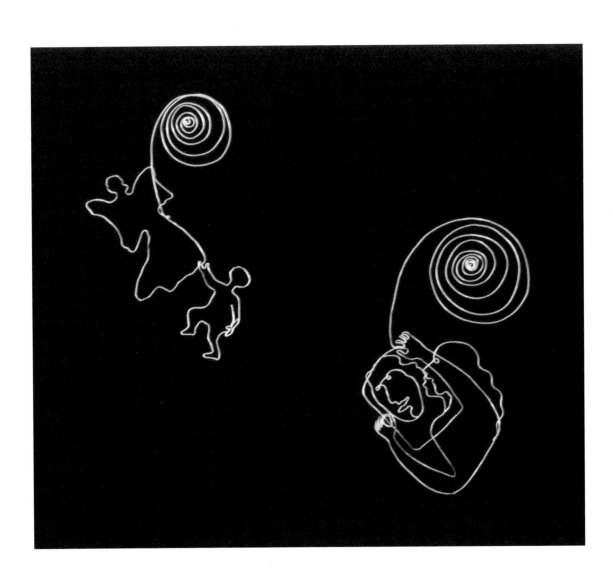

Miria
Wicca-Faery (Pre-Celtic)

*B*efore the beginning—before even the first breath that started the Universe turning—there was wishing.

Just as a pregnant woman longingly awaits the birth of her babe with tender dreaming, so was the Universe conceived of by the fecund imagination of Miria the Wonderful, the Goddess of Creation.

Miria saw her own shining reflected in the dark, curved mirror of the waiting emptiness and she caught her breath, stunned into love for the beauty of her own Self in reflection.

"Oh!"

Her first breath swayed her into motion. Her concentric circles rippled larger and larger, streaming in spirals of light through the darkness towards her mirror image and away, expanding and contracting back and forth.

And so was space created.

Oh!"

Each turn of the gyre was a beat of her longing—now and now and now—and from the pulsing energy came the first tick-tick of time.

"Oh! Oh! Oh!"

Spinning towards her shining double they merged with an ecstatic cry that shook all the realms to be, and Miria gave birth to the world.

Like droplets of light were the spirits of the world born.

The elements emerged: AIR wafted from the sylphs; the gnomes lay down EARTH; nymphs flowed into WATER and salamanders flamed into FIRE.

The faeries turned sunlight into fern and leaf, covering the rotating earth in a mantle of emerald green.

Undines flowed into living streams and restless oceans while the elves led forth the creatures.

Again and again she spun out to her beloved, was met with a shuddering impact and brought back vivid rainbows embossed on cloud, mighty crashes of lightning and thunder, wonder and dreams, laughter and thought, music and memories.

Her song rose to the heights of mist-clothed mountains and spread like mead across islands and lakes.

And again she whirled towards the shining on the opposite shore and recognized it as love itself.

As *Herself*, Miria, who created the world out of love.

And every angel was hand-in-hand with a human child.

Flashing her bright song, Miria spun irresistibly back towards the bright reflection of herself in the curved mirror of space.

"Ohhh-hh!"

Embracing her reflected self and spiraling back to the Source she brought maleness back with her, and the power of opposites.

It was Love that spun the Universe round on its orbit, and Love that sustained life and drew us towards each other and towards the Goddess.

In Love was where all began, and to Love all would seek to return.

Yin and Yang and the Dwarf P'Han ku

China

In the Beginning, before there was Time or an Earth or a Sky, there was *Tao*.

Tao, the mystery of mysteries, the gateway to manifold secrets was the Wholeness from which all separateness was born.

Itself No-Thing, it was the Source of the Ten Thousand Things.

A shaft of pure Light shone out of *Tao* and rose to become the Sky.

The heavier Dark sank to become the Earth.

And the pairs of opposites came into being: Matter and Spirit; Heaven and Earth; Day and Night; Male and Female…
Yin and Yang.

Yin was receptive, soft, intuitive: the feminine principle.

Yang was active, bright, energetic: the masculine principle.

Like lovers they embraced, swirling through the Light and Dark until their very movement formed a shell around them.
An egg.

It was the Cosmic Egg, containing the energies of the Five Elements: Earth, Air, Fire, Water and Wood.

Inside the Cosmic Egg Yin and Yang slept, their essences germinating for Time uncountable, until the World was ready to be born.

When it was time, the Life in the egg was ready to hatch the First Being of the World, P'Han ku.

He pecked hard against the inside of the shell—Bong! Bong!—and the sounds echoed throughout the Cosmos.

Bong! Bong!

The egg cracked open and P'Han ku, a furry, leaf-covered dwarf, came out. Horns of great power sprouted from his hairy head and long tusks curved out from his jaws. Surrounding him in the four corners of the world were his spirit helpers: the Dragon; the Unicorn; the Phoenix; the Tortoise.

In his left hand he held a hammer and in his right hand he held a chisel.

He set to work right away.

With his tools, he hammered out a large, flat plain—the Earth. He placed the Earth carefully upon the Waters and then, with one mighty heave, lifted the Sky up above his head.

Then he chiseled away at the Earth, splitting rocks apart and piling them one upon the other to form the mountains.

Between mist-covered mountains and through green lowlands he sculpted out valleys. Then he dug meandering channels for water to run through.

His work was so beautiful it made him cry, and his tears fell into the riverbeds and flowed all the way down to the sea.

When he breathed hard from all his labors it caused the winds to blow and the clouds to gather in the sky.

When he smiled with gladness, the Sun shone brightly; when he was angry his voice crashed with thunder and brought terrible storms.

When his eyes were open, the day was light; when he slept, the night was dark.

Day after day for 800,000 years P'Han ku continued to create the things of the world.

And each day he grew taller and pushed the Sky up higher and higher, always filling in the space between Earth and Sky with his whole body.

When the Sky, at last, was high enough, he wrote the character for "Moon" in the palm of his left hand.

And he wrote the character for "Sun" in the palm of his right hand.

Then he lifted his arms above his head and, touching the Sky with both palms, called:

SUN SUN SUN SUN SUN SUN SUN!

MOON MOON MOON MOON MOON MOON MOON!

And the Sun and the Moon sprang into the Sky and with them all the stars that shine in the night.

The world was a wonder, but it was far from finished. P'Han ku gazed at his work with satisfaction, but also with sadness, for he knew that everything else needed to complete the world was within his own body.

For he was the child of Yin and Yang.

It was time for him to give his body up as a sacrifice to the world. He surveyed all his creation, climbing his mountains and striding through his meadows; he walked into dense forests and swam in the ocean surf. He gazed at the starry skies and basked in the warmth of his sun.

Sadly, but with pride, he bade his world farewell.

Then, with a sigh that caused the Earth to rumble, he placed his hammer and chisel on the ground and lay down beside them to die.

His skull lifted off his body and rose, giving the Sky its dome shape, and his flesh decomposed, becoming the soil of the fields.

His blood drained into the rivers and lakes and seas, and his sweat became the rain and the mists.

His skin took root and grew into the plants of the world, and his saliva was the morning dew upon them.

His hair, straight and black, turned into all the creatures of the fields and forests. His bushy eyebrows became the birds, and his eyelashes became the fishes.

His bleaching bones turned into rocks and metals, and his semen became droplets of pearls. His bone marrow, turning green, became precious jade and his teeth hardened into diamonds.

On the wind of what had been his breath, and on the thunder of his long-lost voice emerged the microbes and mites and molecules of his flesh. These became human beings—women, men and children.

Loving each other just as their ancestors, Yin and Yang, had loved each other, they were fruitful and multiplied.

Generation after generation they were fruitful. And they peopled the Earth.

The Descendents of Nun
Egypt

Before the first moment of time, there was Nun.

Nun—the primordial waters darker than the darkest night, deeper than the deepest abyss and vaster than all imaginings—lay sleeping.

The Mother-Goddess Nun—womb and heart and mind of All-That-Would -Ever-Be—dreamed. In her silent sleep she dreamed and waited, holding within her depths the hidden potency that would one day make a World.

In her dream she breathed with a longing for Being, and the waters heaved and then billowed. A vaporous mist blew across the dark abyss, an essence searching for substance. The mist gathered into an invisible presence, an imperceptible shape that held within it everything—earth and sky, male and female, water and fire, plant and animal—but was none of these. And yet it was complete in itself. A God.

The God emerged from the agitated waves like a wide-open Eye at the dawning of the world. Dispelling darkness as it rose, it spread its rays from the source of itself, lighting the world around it like a rising Sun. The first God of the world—a Sun to illumine and an Eye to see—was being born.

"Ptah!" the God cried, breaking the surface of the waves and spitting water as he emerged. Gulping for air and calling out the world's first sound, the God heard his own voice echo across the waters.

"Ptah!"

Striking the perfect tone that caused reverberations in the emptiness, the new God sang out the world's first word of power, and by his sound named himself. "Ptah!"

Several times he called out his name. "Ptah!"

Beneath him, the waves crested and tumbled, resonating with his power.

"Out of Nun I have come to Be," he cried, "but where is the foundation upon which to stand?"

He chanted a melody that pulsed to a rhythmic beat. "This is the ground, the beat of Being," he chanted. "This the template, the basic rhythm."

And with his chant a hillock of earth appeared beneath him, and upon this mound he rested. And thus matter was born, and the beginnings of form.

"By my coming into being, Being itself comes into being," he sang, his voice releasing divine harmonies into the brooding silence. "I will create from my heart's desires and my tongue shall call out the spell of creation. With the all-seeing sight of my Eye and the perfect pitch of my voice, I will call everything into being by feeling it in my heart and speaking its Name."

His heard his words sound in the empty silence, and he added more wistfully, "For I am alone here, and lonely."

The Eye on the right side of his forehead, feeling Ptah's yearning for company, projected its sight outwards.

"Seek the secret," Ptah told it, sending the Eye on a search for Others.

When the Eye returned, it resumed its place on the right side of Ptah's forehead and showed him, sight to inner sight, what to do. Ptah received the Eye's instructions with some dismay, but did as he was told.

Joining himself in an embrace with his shadow, he covered his crotch and drew forth his seed. When his seed spurted he bent over to suck the flowing, hot semen into the womb of his mouth, tossing back his head and gargling deep into his throat.

"Shu!" he then cried, blowing out some of his seed. His son Shu, the God of Air and the warmth that makes all Life came flying out of his mouth.

"Tef—nut!" he sputtered, spitting out the rest of his seed through teeth and lips. His daughter Tefnut, the Goddess of Rain and Mist and Clouds and the divine order that makes all universal patterns came flying out next.

Ptah was no longer alone. From One there were now Three—a Trinity—and with Shu and Tefnut he stood upon the hillock and joined hands with them, overjoyed to be with them.

Ptah said to his offspring, "Now that you are here, you shall fill the space above Nun where we shall create the world together."

The Eye began to blink, and hot tears coursed down Ptah's cheek. Then the Eye swelled, growing red and scratchy with anger. The more Ptah rubbed, the more furiously it blinked and the more inflamed it became.

"Ow!" cried Ptah, unable to stop his Eye's enraged demand for attention. "What is the matter?"

"You will supplant me with them?" the Eye challenged. Shu and Tefnut stared balefully at Ptah's forehead. "Now that you've got *them*, I'm not so important anymore?" Blink. Blink.

Ptah, new at the business of creation, glanced quickly at his offspring, who came to the Eye's aid. Shu blew gentle breath on the swollen Eye and Tefnut flushed it with the cool balm of raindrops.

"Quite the contrary," said Ptah breathlessly. "You shall move to the middle of my brow and be the Lord of all Creation. From your place in the center, all things of the world shall be made visible by your Sight." The Eye fluttered and a last burst of tears brimmed over as the Eye's rage fell away and trickled down to its roots.

Each tear, as it hit the ground, became a human child. People of every gender were born—every size and shape and color. And as they were created from the tears of sorrow, all humankind was forevermore to be intimate with suffering.

Under the watchful but non-interfering gaze of the Eye, Shu and Tefnut created the next generation, the twins Geb and Nut—Earth and Heaven. Lying upon one another, Geb and Nut in turn produced Isis and Osiris and Seth and the blind Horus. All of them together began dreaming up the forms of

things: stars and flooding rivers; flowering plants and scuttling beetles; swimming fish and darting birds, jackals and bullocks, falcons and palm trees.

As one form after another, like droplets of Nun each in its own distinctive vessel, took its place amongst them, the hillock became rather chaotic with all of them crowded there together. It was too much life in too small a space. The clamor was deafening and the Gods began to fight with each other. Shu and Tefnut held their hands over their ears.

Then Shu blew out a mighty wind to separate Nut from Geb, lifting his daughter into a graceful arch over her brother, making space for the world to grow. The stars found their place in Nut and the things of the Earth found their place in Geb, just as it was envisioned in Nun.

Heaven was now above, and Earth below. And the sustained sound of their father's wind—an echo of Ptah's song which resonated from the dream of Nun—were like pillars joining Heaven with Earth, holding all of the world in perfect balance.

From the Edge of the World
Baja Mexico ~ Seri

In the beginning, there was no land and no life, only the fathomless sea and Yooz, the pure force from which all things would come. Yooz, knowing all, existed everywhere at once and with his Eye, the Sun, he watched from the Sky, and saw all that there was.

Yooz contained everything—everything that was or would ever be. Within him was the Maker, Hant Caai, from whom all things would be created and the Namer, Hant Quizim, from whom all things would receive a sound—a name. And from whom Light would be made visible in the world.

The pure force that was Yooz breathed in and all was silence. The pure force that was Yooz breathed out and the stillness broke into song. From the edge of the world the song brought forth zigzags of lightning which crashed and streaked in every direction, thundering and roaring and clapping at the Sky and the Sea. The song brought wonder to the silent world; the song of Yooz breathed pure spirit into the world.

Reaching beyond the edge of the world, Hant Caai brought forth the first animals, placing them onto a raft woven of rush in the middle of the ocean. He made dolphins and whales to swim in the deeps and multitudes of fish to swim in the waves. He made deer and bighorn sheep for the mountains, and coyotes and badgers and rabbits for the deserts. He made shellfish and crabs for the rockbound shorelines and stingrays to skim through the shallows.

Birds he made for the air—pelicans, mockingbirds, gulls—but more than anything he made tortoises: fourteen different kinds for the sea and for the land.

When the raft was filled with all the creatures of the sea and the land, Hant Caai said to the animals,

"I will need the help of one of you to dive down and bring back to me some of the rich mud that lies at the bottom of the ocean. With that mud, I shall create the land."

Land Tortoise went first, plopping over the side of the raft and paddling with all her might towards the bottom. But the ocean was very deep, and no matter how hard she pushed herself, she could not reach the floor of the sea. Even after a year of swimming she had still not reached bottom and so, very tired, she gave up and came gasping to the surface with no rich mud to show for her efforts.

Next, Green Sea Turtle tried. He slipped over the side of the raft and with powerful flippers he breasted his way towards the bottom. One year passed, and then two…For five years he kept going down and down until, one day when his strength was just about gone his claws scraped the rich mud of the bottom of the sea. With one scoop he caught some between his claws before he exhaustedly turned and, pushing off, started the long ascent back to the surface.

Gasping, he emerged from the waves. Hant Caai grasped Green Sea Turtle's flippers and hauled him over the side of the raft, carefully gathering the bits of mud clinging to his claws and rolling it into a small, wet ball. This precious ball of mud he flattened out and smoothed onto the carapace of Giant Leatherback Turtle, singing as he spread the earthy paste.

The mud, no matter how much he pressed and spread it, remained soft to the touch, so Hant Caai created a long-legged spider to test the earth's firmness. Singing another song, he dropped the spider onto the mud to see if it could walk, but the spider just sank into the tacky soil and stuck there. The land would have to be hardened.

Hant Quizim, the hardener of the land, breathed in and leapt onto the back of Giant Leatherback Turtle. Dancing, his feet beat out a steady rhythm as he sang a song of power and drummed the land into firmness with his pounding steps.

The land sizzled with the heat of Hant Quizim's dance and it gradually hardened, shaped into ridges and plains, islands and seashores. It was sacred earth that formed on the back of Giant Leatherback Turtle, and was surrounded by the waters of the world.

Beneath the hardened land—where the earth touched the Turtle's back—lay the realm of the spirits. And hidden within the land were tiny openings—caves—through which those spirits might be reached.

Valleys formed and tall mountains; deserts stretched far, and came right down to the sea. And the land itself began to sing its song:

Watch me dance!
See where I place my steps.
I dance right here upon this shore
A dance that is in perfect balance.
If I make even one step out of place
The whole world will turn right over!

And the land settled, creaking and groaning itself into the balance of an Earth. From the Sky came whirring whirlwinds, spinning down to touch the land, and the winds started—seven kinds of wind which sighed or roared or whispered—and the land's dust was raised into the air. Hant Caai listened to each of the wind's sounds and transformed each into a different plant: low hummings became the barrel cactus; high pings, like rain, became the yellow flowers of the xojat plant in Spring.

While the land sustained its soft roar, life's aliveness sang in many tones, popping and whirring and hissing into being.

Hant Quizim named each growing thing as it appeared.

"Mesquite!" he sang. "Cardon! Saguaro! Desert lavender!"

Whooshes of surf spilled onto the shore and flowing eelgrass strands appeared in the waves, singing its own song.

My watery stems spread and curl
In the waves' ebb and flow.
But I am not moving water; I am not waves of
the sea!

Eelgrass would be food for the people who were to come. It was almost time for The Maker—Hant Caai—to bring forth the people.

The shimmering world looked good and was ready for First Man and First Woman.

He listened for the sound of the Bursera tree, which would provide shade for the people, and then sang it into being. Shaded by its leaves, he searched the horizon at the edge of the world for the coming of the first people.

She looked tiny at first—the First Woman— as she appeared in the distance at the edge of the world, but as she approached closer to the Bursera tree, Hant Caai could see that she was a giantess, bright blue and beautiful to behold. She strode towards the tree on strong, shapely legs as tall as the Bursera tree itself.

"First Woman!" sang Hant Quizim, as she calmly took her place beneath the branches of the tree.

"First Man!" Hant Quizim cried as there appeared another giant from the other edge of the world who, in a few enormous steps, reached the other side of the Bursera tree to join his partner. Lights and colors shot out from Earth and Sky, zigzagging every which way around the First Couple like lightning.

A wondrous power touches me, sang First Woman. *It reaches through the Sky from the other side of the world. A wondrous power touches me.*

And First Man sang,

A wondrous power touches me. It reaches through the Sky from the other side of the world. A wondrous power touches me.

Then the First Couple bent down to scoop out a long trench in the sand, lying down in it where the shimmering heat of the Sun—Yooz—would cover them. The hot, fecund rays beat down upon them, filling First Woman with the seed for the first seven generations of humankind that would people the world.

But before the first race of giants to inhabit the earth could be born, Hant Caai had to test First Man and First Woman, to make sure they would provide well for the people. So he sang the sound for Horse, and when it was created, he placed it beneath the Bursera tree. Then he made a balsa, a reed boat, to rock in the waves.

"Mount the horse, and ride," Hant Caai told First Man, not showing him how to do it. First Man eyed the horse warily, grasping its rump and jumping onto its back. But he slipped right off the other side, and the horse pranced restively. He tried to steady the horse with a giant hand, but it walked easily out from under him. Then First Man grasped its mane and flung a giant leg over its back, hauling himself unsteadily up until he was on—facing its tail!

Horse took off at a trot, jouncing its backwards-rider up and down until First Man's teeth rattled in his mouth and he lost his balance and tumbled to the ground with a great Thump! First Woman burst into peals of laughter, but Hant Caai simply nodded, reigned in the Horse and said to First Man,

"Take the balsa out to sea and spear a green turtle." First Man picked himself up off the ground, red-faced, and not looking at First Woman, strode purposefully into the surf and climbed into the reed boat. He balanced it by holding onto both sides as he stepped in, first one foot and then the other. Steering skillfully, he rode the boat over the breaking lines of surf until he was out in open water and paddling vigorously. Hant Caai watched approvingly.

"Bring back a green turtle!" he called out to First Man, who was already scanning the waves for the telltale shadow beneath the surface. It was not long before a great arm shot out from the balsa like a spear, capturing a furious beast. First Man hauled it over the side, sat squarely on its back and paddled back to the shore, triumphant.

"Aahssah!" said Hant Caai as First Man beached the reed boat. "Now you must butcher the beast so that you and First Woman can provide for all the children that shall come."

First Man gazed around him, wondering what he might use for a knife. He picked up a rounded stone from the beach, but it had no edge to it and he tossed it back down again. Then he strode into the desert and found a reed plant with long canes, which he plucked, peeled and split with his teeth into sharp-edged stalks. Returning to the shore with his cutting knife, he set about butchering the turtle.

"Although you failed the first test," said Hant Caai, "you have passed the second test well. It is clear that you would be useless working the land, but you shall make an excellent fisherman. From the sea, you and First Woman shall support all your children."

Then Hant Caai turned to First Woman and told her,

"You are to give birth to the People. Four clans shall you produce: The Turtle Clan, The Coyote Clan, The Cactus Pear Clan and The Pelican Clan. You shall be the mother of giants who will inhabit the earth—tall enough to wade through the ocean to other land; large enough to have bees nest between their teeth, so that honey shall drip from their mouths when they smile! With your nurturance and guidance they shall thrive and multiply."

He went on, "There will be floods and there will be fires and there will be earthquakes. Many devastations shall test your children, but they shall learn how to transform themselves so they will always survive."

And First Woman, with the heat and the seed of the Sun within her, rested her hands gently upon her swelling belly and knew it would always be so.

Dreaming the World into Being
Australian Aborigine

Before time began, there was Dreaming. In the vast, unbounded Darkness beneath the Earth and Above the Sky there was Yingarna, Dreaming. Yingarna was the All-Mother and All-Father, the ageless and unaging web of vital force that contained the promise of All-Creation. Yingarna was the clear crystal and the rainbow waters, the Divine Couple, the Creative Ancestors.

The Dreaming.

Dark and silent, He/She contained the in-breath for Light and the out-breath for Sound.

Eternal and still, She/He held the promised tick-tick of Time and the first impulse for motion.

Single and Whole, He/She was pregnant with the potential for birth and the countless multitudes to be created upon the Earth.

Dreaming, the Creative Ancestors felt a yearning to know their coming Creation, and the seed-force of their longing sparked into existence a Rainbow Serpent deep within the womb of the All-Mother. In the dark cave of the womb, the Rainbow Serpent curled and stretched, the purple and blue and green and yellow and orange and red of its body still invisible. It was Male and it was Female and, containing every possibility of form and function in its being, the Rainbow Serpent would be the Source of All-That-Would-Come. The currents of its energy would shape mountains and oceans and continents onto every surface of the Earth.

Heartbeat by heartbeat, it would awaken all Life into being.

At a whisper from the All-Father, the Rainbow Serpent gently uncoiled its multi-colored body. The still waters were stirred into roiling motion and from the Deeps came a profound shifting as, with great cracks and heaves, the continents lifted and spilled cataracts of water and rock back into the ocean. Groaning with effort, the bodies of the land at last floated face up into the air, their buttocks in water and their surfaces empty and flat. They were almost ready to be filled with stories. It was the First Day and time to move from the unchanging Dreamtime to a living world with its winds and changes.

Twisting and turning to be born through layers of darkness, the Rainbow Serpent emerged from the womb of the All-Mother into the air of the world. She gulped in her first breath and her exhalation vibrated the air, shaking it into gusts and breezes. Currents of wind tumbled her and she opened her eyes, spinning round and round as the darkness dispersed and she became a golden orb radiant with light. With each breath she grew larger and hotter, and with each turn of her great body she sent rays of multicolored light and heat deeper into the darkness, warming and illuminating the land.

By being born, the Rainbow Serpent was transformed into the Sun Mother from whom all life would come.

Sun Mother set out to the North and to the South, to the East and to the West to survey the land that would support the living world. The earth lay flat and barren beneath her, but she knew that beneath its brown crust, in hollows and small caves, lay slumbering all the Dreamtime Ancestors of the universe. They were the guruwari—the patterns of conscious energy which lay beneath every rock and hill, every tree and plant, every animal and person that would ever exist upon the Earth.

As Sun Mother approached each place on the land, the Dreamtime Ancestors felt her warming rays upon their unused limbs and motionless sap, and their awareness quickened into life.

Sun Mother cried, "May my naming reach to the belly of the Sky!" She asked that the eternal soul of the universe be reflected in every changing body to exist upon the land. "May the Earth be the belly of the Sky!"

At one hillock of red earth she called the trees into being.

"Ancestor Ironwood!" she sang. "Ancestor Eucalyptus! Ancestor Sandalwood!" And each one sprang from the navel and armpits of the earth, woody and green and strong. They stabilized their essential natures by singing back to her the seed-sounds of their names, calling,

"I *AM* Ancestor Ironwood! I *AM* Ancestor Eucalypus! I *AM* Ancestor Sandalwood!"

She moved on, warming the Dreamtime Ancestors of the vines into life, and those of the flowers.

"Ancestor Brigalow!" she called. "Ancestor Lantana! Ancestor Orchid! Ancestor Rock lily!" And they sang back to her their names as they sent sprouts up through the crust of the earth and unfurled into green leaf and fragrant flower. Honey-ants tickled over the ground on tiny fast feet. Spiders spun themselves out of silken webs. Snakes and the fishes slithered and wriggled themselves into scaled things, drawing watercourses behind them. River Ancestor flowed into many streams and the water pooled into basins, gurgling and splashing as each was named into being.

"Ancestor Brook! Ancestor Billibong! Ancestor Lagoon! Ancestor Creek!" The Sun Mother sent the sound of their names into the ground, laying down lines of song-potency as she traversed the land, singing and naming.

"Ancestors Koala! Kangaroo! Cassowary! Bandicoot!"

"Ancestors Spider! Ant! Wallabye! Flying fox!"

"Ancestors Wombat! Kookaburra! Wonga-wonga! Lyre-bird!"

"Ancestors Cockatoo! Gang-gang! Chat-chat! Tallegulla!"

And as each Dreamtime Ancestor was awakened from its sleep and called out its name in response to the Sun Mother, the air was filled with moos and yaps and growls and croons and barks and coo-ees. With their living breaths and footfalls, their fighting and their feeding and their mating, they began to shape the barren land into mountains and plains, hillocks and hollows, salt pans and fault escarpments.

For with each moment of living and with each sleeping dream, they created upon the earth a crisscrossing chorus of many-voiced sound, like the humming network of blood running in their veins. And so began the story of life in the world.

From the red-earthed ridges there appeared a dreaming within the larger Dreaming. It was like a memory evoked from deep within the Ancestors, of two-legged beings whose spirits flew like birds, who hunted and gathered hungrily like marsupials and mammals, who lusted and played, laughed and wept like gods.

It was because of the Ancestors' desire to clothe their longings in human bodies and bring into the physical world the ecstasy of their ageless souls that People were created.

The People were endowed with keen sight and patience, and the capacity for tenderness, bliss and rage. Their voices could sing and their feet could stamp in rhythmic dance, leaving imprints of their passing in the sand. In every way they were created perfect, their beauty maturing as the hard experiences of lives well-lived left their marks. Their task on Earth would be to maintain the perfection of the world by listening to it closely and thus understanding how to reflect its natural laws.

It was mid-day of the First Day and Sun Mother rose into the zenith of the Sky, scorching the Earth with shimmering waves of heat. Watercourses dried up, the air was still and the creatures crawled into the shade of bushes and lairs. The Season of Summer was created.

When Sun Mother moved lower in the Sky, her rays reached the Earth at a slant and the rains came, filling the waterholes and soaking all the seedpods waiting to be quickened by wetness. The people, matching their movements to the Seasons of the Sun Mother and to the habits of the plant and animal Ancestors tracked and hunted the quick-footed creatures, plucked nuts from the trees and dug deep in the Earth for juice-filled roots.

It was the end of the First Day and Sun Mother rested at the Western horizon in a flush of red and pink. The Sky held all the colors of her Rainbow body, but the Moon and Star and Planet Ancestors still lay in slumber beneath the Earth.

"Ancestor Moon!" she called. "Ancestors of the Stars! Ancestors of the Planets!" They awoke from their sleep and rode upon her pulsing rays to her place at the Western horizon. From there she flung them, one by one, into the Sky. With a last flicker of a smile before sinking beneath the curve of the Earth, she listened for the harmony of the World vibrating in her being. It rang true and clear on this First Day of Creation.

"May every day be the First Day of Creation," she prayed, "and may every moment of life upon the Earth be a new beginning." And with that prayer, she went under.

In moments, the world was plunged into darkness again. The Animal and Plant and Human Ancestors huddled together for company, trying to choose one of them to call back the Sun.

"Sing her Name!" one suggested, attempting a long howl. Another sang a plaintive nightsong; one whuffled loudly and another chirruped with all her heart.

But no sound brought back the Sun Mother—until much later in the night, when Ancestor Jackass tried. Giving a braying snort of laughter, and setting all the others in raucous chorus of giggles and cheers, Jackass caused the Sun to emerge with a faint glowing at first, but then more and more until, from the Eastern edge of the world, the world again was lit.

The creatures cheered the Sun Mother with roars and laughter, welcoming her back into their midst and deciding that it would be Jackass who would laugh out to her after every time of darkness. He agreed, but said it would be his progeny for the rest of Time who would laugh her back as he, like the rest of the Dreamtime Ancestors was growing tired. Sighing deeply, he sank towards the Earth, laying his weary head against a hillock of red earth while his children pranced about him on the ground.

Dreamtime Ancestors Kangaroo and Wallabye, Koala and Snake, Cassowary and Bandicoot—each trod to its place on the Earth—hollow and cave and salt pan— and went back in, merging with it for the rest of Time.

They left behind them the seeds for the coming generations who sprouted up in their place, and a wash of subtle music along the songlines they had walked.

Upon this web of song made by their footprints, all of us would live and love and die—just as the Ancestors had done. And would never forget their undying presence— even while they slumbered—as we heard the timeless echoes of their many-voiced song.

Lumimu'ut and Her Son Toar
Indonesia (Sulawesi)

In the beginning, there was only water— primordial, seething sea everywhere. And one jutting bit of rock.

The cone of dark rock, wreathed in cloud, just crested the waves. From deep within the rock molten fire rose, steaming. The steam cooled as it hit the air, turning into rain that fell upon the rock, pooling into cracks and seeping down its sides. Rock-sweat.

Steaming air and falling rain swirled together, becoming the feather and form of Hornbill Crane. Above the vast sea Hornbill Crane took flight, circling the steaming rock, watching the steaming rock until a Goddess began to emerge from it. From the moisture of the rock's sweat Lumimu'ut, Mother of Earth and all things, was born. She, Lumimu'ut, emerged from water and rock and slid down into Life.

Hornbill Crane cawed down to her,

"You are here to create an Earth from the original land at the bottom of the sea! Listen to me!"

Lumimu'ut listened, not knowing how to begin. She gazed up at Hornbill Crane. "How?" she called

"Look to the waters of the world!"

Nights passed, and days. Lumimu'ut, listening and waiting on the edge of the rock, stared intently at the seething waters. They gave no clue until, up from the primal, dark deeps arose Turtle, swimming to the rock. In one claw and in her beak she held sacred mud from the original land at the bottom of the sea. The mud in her claw was black; the clay in her beak was red. Placing the original soil at Lumimu'ut's feet, she dove down again to bring back more.

Lumimu'ut picked up the black mud and the red clay and smoothed it all over the rock. When Turtle returned with more soil, Lumimu'ut began to shape a world. The rock took on height and breadth. Lumimu'ut fashioned mountains and deep valleys. The soil was sculpted into hills and plains, volcanoes and islands. Turtle dived, bringing more clay, more mud of the original land, and Lumimu'ut scooped out rivers, lay down forests, and spread grasses and scrub and flowering trees on lowland and highland alike.

When the world was complete, Turtle dragged herself onto the shore of the world and lay there weeping saltwater tears, exhausted with her efforts.

Lumimu'ut sat down beside her on the land they had created together, and they both slept. When she awoke, she knew it was time to create the Gods so taking her staff of gnarled wood, she went to the base of the world's tallest mountain and began to climb. Nights passed, and days. When she reached the highest pinnacle of the mountain the sun was setting in a rich red and yellow sky. The mountain turned green, then mauve, then purple. She felt a quickening in her heart and, laughing, she spread wide her arms to the sky and gave herself ecstatically to the West Wind.

The West Wind grabbed her up playfully, teasingly buffeting her and blowing her hair wildly about her face. She caught her breath and turned, leaning into him and then letting him chase her in pursuit. She leapt into him and crouched away from him, shouting as he howled and opening to him as he blew.

And from their union came the Gods. They coupled again to create the first human, whose line would maintain the balance between the upper world of the Gods, and the lower world of the earth and sea. Lumimu'ut, by coupling with the West Wind became Mother to the Gods and the First Ancestor of all humans.

From their union was conceived Toar, the First Man.

The years passed, and when Toar came of age his mother Lumimu'ut told him it was time to leave home and circle the earth.

"Walk around this world, going from East to West," she said, "and search for your partner with whom to people the Earth. Look for a woman, like me—one who is shorter than my staff."

Lumimu'ut measured the gnarled length of wood against her side. It came up to her cheekbone.

She kissed her son and sent him off walking to the West. She leaned upon her staff, gazing at his retreating back until he was a dot upon the horizon. Then, sighing, she turned around and took her first step around the world in the other direction, walking from West to East.

For time out of time, mother and son walked around the world, each in opposite directions. Toar grew sinewy and strong. His eyes grew sharp as the eyes of a sea eagle and his legs as massive as the trunks of trees, while his mind filled with the sights of the world.

Lumimu'ut grew older, wisdom gathering in her heart and her skin growing leathery with sun. Seasons passed, and untold numbers of moons. Her body grew bent, her bones settling gradually towards her feet. Her skin loosened, wrinkling about her shrinking body.

Climbing to the summit of Mount Nunusaku, halfway around the world, Toar stopped to rest beneath an overhanging rock ledge. He lay himself down and spread out his arms, sighing. Sleeping, he failed to notice that a woman, arriving from the opposite side of the mountain, reached the summit shortly after he did. She gazed down at his sleeping figure, noting with satisfaction how strong he had become, how beautiful. Her heart ached for him—as mother and as woman.

"Look for me—I am here," she sang softly, beneath her breath.

Waking, Toar saw a mature woman standing by his side and he jumped up. She was quite a bit shorter than his mother's staff, and he loved her on sight and knew that this was the woman he would take as his wife.

"Come," he said gently, taking the staff from her hands, still not recognizing that this woman was his mother grown older. "Lie with me here. Then we shall descend the mountain to make our home in the world."

Lumimu'ut, a small smile playing about her lips, sank to the good earth that she had made, smelling its fragrance of sun-warmed stone and sweet soil. Closing her eyes she dreamed of the children they would create together—the half-heaven, half-earth beings who would reside in the world.

And she dreamed of the Nine Families from whom all those beings would come: the Buffalo Clan; the Fish Clan; the Butterfly Clan; the Deer Clan; the Bird Clan; the Clam Clan; the Crab Clan; the Crocodile Clan and the Turtle Clan. And so it was.

Adrienne and Carolyn at the Brattleboro Museum. Appliqued wall hanging by Carolyn.

Creation Chant
Mali ~ The Fulani People

From the Primal Chaos

Was the Mother of All Things made.

From the breast of the mother

Came the first drop of milk.

From the drops of milk

Was the God Doondari fed.

He grew strong and stronger

Until he was hard as stone.

The stone, hardening more

Became as pure as metal.

The metal, melting,

Became flashing hot fire.

The fire, flowing, cooled into water.

The water, steaming, dissolved into air.

In the Beginning has appeared on exhibition
at the following venues:

The Winsor School, Boston
The Spence School, New York City
The Meetinghouse Center for Theology and the Arts,
    Andover Newton Theological School, Boston
First and Second Unitarian Church, Boston
The University Lutheran Church Gallery, Cambridge
The Clara Wainright Gallery, Boston
The Paine Art Center and Arboretum, Oshkosh, Wisconsin
The Brattleboro Museum and Art Center,
    Brattleboro, Vermont
Santa Sabina Retreat Center, San Rafael, California

ACKNOWLEDGMENTS

For our stays in the country,
we would like to thank
Barbara Valocore
Thomas Fricke and Sylvia Blanchet
the late Snoo Heslen
Tim Hayes and Pam Bullock
Pamela Mayer
Mr. and Mrs. Herbert Hayes

To Adriel Heisey who led us to the Seri Myth, and to
Brenda Dunne who led us to ICRL Press.

Illustrations

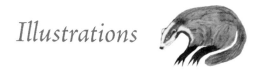

GENESIS
Void, paper, acrylic paints, 10" x 12"
Light and Dark, acrylic paints on paper, 12" x 12"
Green Plants, collage, acrylic paints on paper, 10" x 18"
Flowers, collage on paper, 10" x 18"
Sea Creatures, collage on paper, 14" x 15"
Creatures of the Earth, collage on paper, 13" x 12"
Human Races of the Earth, collage on paper,
12" diameter

IROQUOIS NATION
Papier mache, acrylic paints, 10" x 11" (closed),
15½" x 21" (fully opened)

AFRICAN BUSHMAN
Papier mache, collage, acrylic paint, 10" x 18"

WABENAKI PEOPLES
Seeds, beans, pods, leaves, pine needles, feathers,
bones, sea shells, pebbles and rocks, paper wasps' nest,
moss, crab shell, nuts and sand on masonite,
40" diameter

GREECE
Cardboard on masonite, collage and acrylic paints,
32" diameter

JAPAN
Handmade Japanese printed papers and rice paper,
38" x 53"

INDIA
Sari silk, patterned Indian papers, 27" x 32"

QUICHE MAYA
Layered felt, cut collage, 6' x 4½'

PRE-CELTIC
Wire on black felt, 35" x 28"

CHINA
Handmade patterned papers, collage, 18" x 24"

EGYPT
Wire, beads, stones on black felt, 38" x 67½"

BAJA MEXICO
Acrylic paint on paper, 30½" x 57"

ABORIGINAL AUSTRALIA
Water-based ink print on paper, 18" x 24"

INDONESIA
Goat skin, acrylic paints
Male Puppet, 23" x 12"
Mountain, 22 x 16
Female Puppet, 19" x 12"

MALI
Mixed fabric

CPSIA information can be obtained
at www.ICGtesting.com
Printed in the USA
LVIC07n1257190713
343445LV00007B